FOLKTALES AND LEGENDS OF EAST ANGLIA

by Geoffrey Dixon
and
Lynn Green

Published by Mininax Books Ltd

ISBN 0 906791 81 2

Broadgate House
Church Street
Deeping St James
Peterborough PE6 8HD
England

Printed in England

CONTENTS

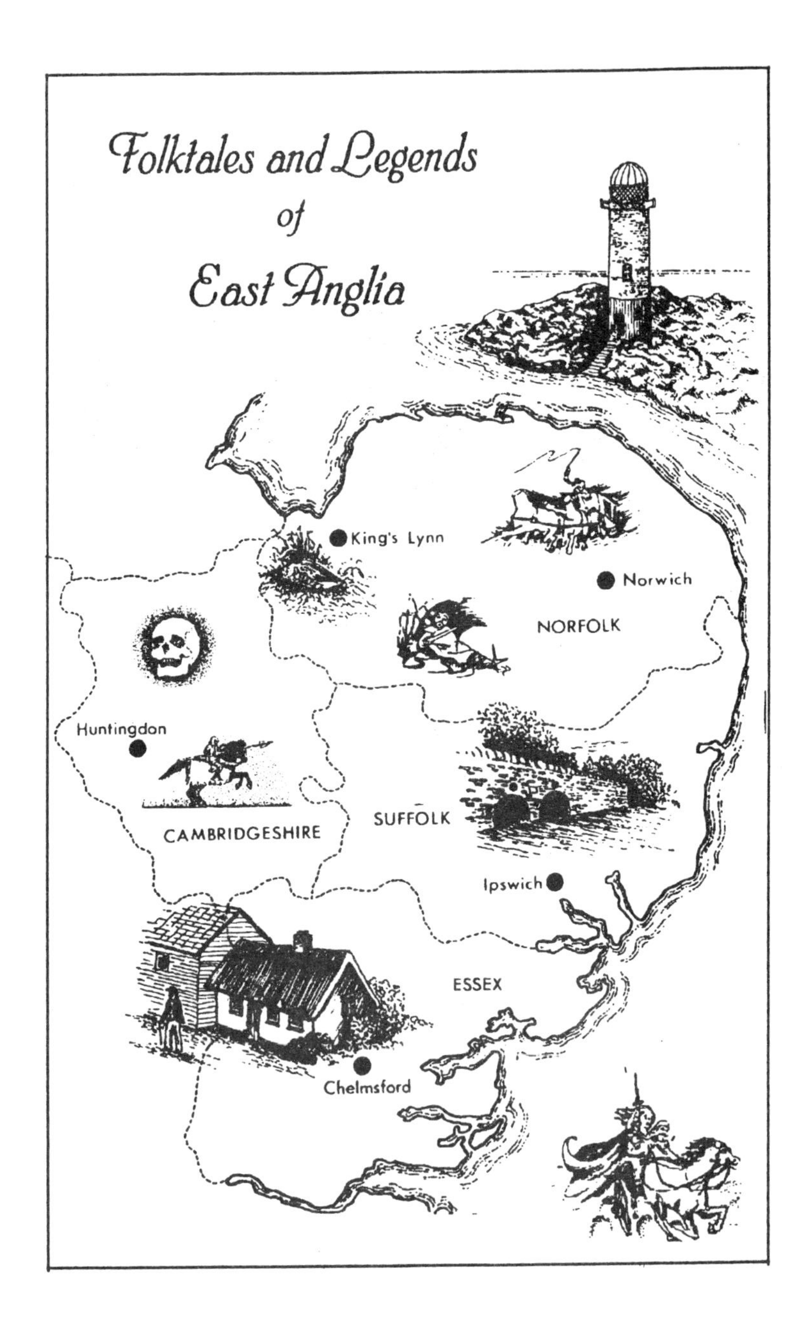
Folktales and Legends
of
East Anglia
King's Lynn
Norwich
NORFOLK
Huntingdon
CAMBRIDGESHIRE
SUFFOLK
Ipswich
ESSEX
Chelmsford

CONTENTS continued ....

JABEZ'S MICE

Willingham, in Cambridgeshire, is noted for its windmills, orchards and fine church. Earthworks survive on the drained marshes and the place seems full of history, but it is a story from this century that is particularly worth telling.

Most of us think that the days of witches, goblins, imps and such like are long gone - their death knell being sounded by the enlightenment of modern science. So, would you be surprised to hear that, within living memory, evidence of the strangely supernatural is well documented? For example, a study of the Cambridgeshire newspapers of the early 1920s will reveal a strange, eerie story, gripping because of its sheer earthiness. Read on.

In a little cottage, down one of the lanes in Willingham, lived old Jabez Few, who worked on a local farm as a horseman. He was a harmless looking old man, with a pair of bright eyes, a bushy beard and a short but substantial stature. His wife had died when she was quite young, leaving Jabez with two teenage sons to bring up. Both were caught up in the Boer War in the early years of this century, one losing his life at Rorke's Drift and the other staying out in South Africa to farm. This left Jabez alone, apart from a sister living in a neighbouring village.

Mr Few had an extensive knowledge of herbs and potions and often used his skills to bring cures to his beloved horses. Occasionally, as a special favour, he would furnish a medicinal mix for an acquaintance.

To all intents and purposes, Jabez lived a quiet and unremarkable life but people said that he went 'a bit funny' when he lost his wife and, soon after, his sons. Others attributed his eccentricity to his lonely lifestyle but some ascribed his strangeness to a more sinister source. Was there not evil in his glances? Why did he shun company? What was he afraid of? What did he have to hide? And so the suspicion started and the gossiping worsened.

The few people who went to the cottage came back speaking of mice running free there, unmolested and with disregard to Jabez and themselves. It was only a short time before it became 'known' that these mice were his imps and that Jabez had an amazing power over them. People spoke of these matters in hushed whispers, so that the children should not hear.

Chief amongst those who gossiped continually of old Jabez and his evil ways was Mrs Pratt, who lived just down the road from him. At the mention of his name, and sometimes without, Mrs Pratt gushed forth with quite ludicrous tales. She delighted in the authority that her stories brought and, whilst people did not know whether or not to believe her, they muttered that there could be no smoke without fire.

Of course Jabez knew of Mrs Pratt and her prattle and was determined to put an end to it by frightening her. So he got a mouse, one of the biggest that he could find, and took it in his pocket to Mrs Pratt's gate. He took the mouse out, stroked it in his hand, muttered quietly in its ear, put it gently on the ground and watched it scuttle along the path and under Mrs Pratt's door. Once indoors, it delighted in finding Mrs Pratt's dearest possessions and nibbling at them. Her best Sunday cake, the newly embroidered chairback, a wall picture of Queen Victoria, her best linen sheets, the curtains at her windows, a piece of cheese favoured by Mr Pratt: all these and more the large mouse found and ruined.

Mrs Pratt was soon desperate for help and called on her friend, Mrs Rayner, to ask if she could borrow her cat, Hector. Hector was a large, three year old tom cat, fur shining with health and in peak condition. Mrs Rayner lent her cat gladly, secretly pleased to become involved. She confidently assured

Mrs Pratt that Hector would rid her of the mouse and put the cat into the gossip's arms.

On arriving home, Hector was put straight into the bedroom where Mrs Pratt had seen unmistakable evidence of the mouse not thirty minutes before. The candles on her dressing table had been chewed and mouse droppings were left nearby to add insult to injury!

The cat dived immediately under the bed and Mrs Pratt came out, closing the door behind her. She called down to her husband to come upstairs and, surprised by this unfamiliar invitation, he hurried up the steps. As his wife finished telling him what she was doing, there came the sound of violent fighting behind the door and Mrs Pratt feared for her possessions. After a while the noise subsided and, with a pleasing sense of anticipation, Mrs Pratt opened the door. The room was in disarray, but what caused husband and wife to gasp in shock was the sight of the cat. Stripped of half its fur, it was clinging to the curtains. In dismay, Mrs Pratt hurriedly returned Hector to Mrs Rayner's house where he remained, a nervous whimpering wreck, for the rest of his days.

Mr Pratt decided on positive action and he went out to gather herbs from the hedgerows, clippings of horses' hoof from the blacksmith and the back legs off some poor toad! He took these home and was boiling them in a stone jar on the kitchen fire. Word of such things spread rapidly in villages and soon Jabez Few heard of it and hurried round to the Pratt's gateway. From behind the drawn curtains they heard Jabez whistle loudly and, when they peeped, they saw the mouse scuttling up the path and into his hands.

Strange? Certainly. Unbelievable? Yes, but Mr and Mrs Pratt assure us that it happened and this is not the end of the tale.

When Jabez died, his cottage passed into the ownership of his nephew and he could only get rid of the resident mice by holding them over running water, after which they ran away and vanished.

The old cottage where Mr Few lived has changed hands several times and has been extensively restored of late. Its whereabouts will not be disclosed, however, because it is best to let sleeping mice lie.

Satan Visits Thomasina

This story, from the fenland village of Haddenham, involves mice and the houseproud Myrtle Lines in the year 1647.

There had been quite a plague of mice in the village and the cats were kept extremely busy. One place that the mice seemed to be welcomed was the cottage belonging to Thomasina Read, and it was rumoured that she attracted them on purpose. Gossippy Myrtle Lines went to investigate and Thomasina told her, quite brazenly, that the devil visited her in the form of one particular fat mouse. She knew it to be the devil because one day it climbed under her skirts, up her stockings and bit her at the top of her right leg. She claimed to be able to use the mouse, after it had bitten and sucked her blood, to bewitch people. Indeed, she said that the mouse had sucked blood from her left arm then caused Thomas Condron to have fits because he laughed at Thomasina. Myrtle Lines was horrified and went to the village Leet to tell her story.

Thomasina was brought before the Leet and questioned but denied all charges, showing her unmarked left arm and right leg in proof. She claimed that Myrtle Lines was just a trouble maker, and was allowed to go home. Once there, however, Thomasine pushed up her right sleeve, smiled, scratched at the itchy teeth marks and called for the big mouse to come up on to her lap. How could she pay back Myrle Lines?

THE HEADLESS HORSEMAN OF BLICKLING HALL

Stories of headless horsemen, presagers of death,
are reasonably common but one has its origin at the
beautiful mansion at Blickling, near Aylsham.
Blickling Hall is now owned by the National Trust,
having been donated to them by the Marquis of Lothian.
Visit it now, on a warm summer day;
soak up the wonderful atmosphere, and think back to
the dark days of Henry VIII.

When Henry VIII ordered the execution of Anne Boleyn, he had more pressing matters on his mind than the fate of her father.

Catherine of Aragon was only able to bear Henry a daughter, destined to be the unpopular Mary I, and as a consequence of this he turned his attention to Anne Boleyn, a lady-in-waiting. He found, in her, a ready and worthy accomplice, a lively and spirited companion, and hope for the future. Henry could have kept Anne as his mistress but, like all monarchs of that era, wanted a legitimate son to succeed him. Therefore, he needed to marry Anne and have an acknowledged successor to the throne.

Thus Henry of England courted Anne and, with his counsellors, devised ways of breaking his marriage to Catherine. The Church, of course, would not sanction divorce, and Henry had to break with the Roman Catholic Church in order to rid himself of his unwanted wife.

Sir Thomas Boleyn was delighted when his beautiful daughter was originally accepted at Court, and even more so when she became the preferred one of the King. Proudly he stepped around his estates at Blickling, boasting of his connections at the Royal Court. Little did he realise what the future held for both himself and his daughter.

After Henry's divorce and subsequent marriage to Anne, Sir Thomas Boleyn became a favoured visitor at court and was held in awe, as the father of the Queen, by all who worked for him on his lands in Norfolk. Anne gave birth to a daughter, Elizabeth, but not to the longed for son. Perhaps her father foresaw her fate, but surely he could not have predicted the callousness of Henry VIII who had Anne put to death on a trumped up charge of treachery.

Sir Thomas Boleyn did not attend the execution of his daughter but fled to his estates at Blickling where he went into hiding, a sadly deflated man He was told that she smiled at the gentleman who brought her from the room in the Tower of London, saying, "I hear the executioner is very skilful; my neck is very small."

The horror of Anne's death haunted him and he became obsessed by the thought of heads being severed from bodies. His mind must have played with the thought for, when he died, six years later, he made a vow: "For that cruel death I will lose my head, and the country will know it. For the eleven years she was with me are eleven bridges to my happiness and I will cross them for a thousand years to regain that pleasure and so that my soul may rest."

And so Sir Thomas died, as he had lived, tormented by the knowledge that he had facilitated her marriage and therefore her death.

On May 19th each year, until 2036, the headless ghost of Sir Thomas, driving a coach pulled by four headless horses, crosses the eleven bridges at Aylsham, Burgh, Oxnead, Buxton, Hautbois, Coltishall, Belaugh, the two at Meyton and at Wroxham, in an attempt to atone for the death of his daughter. As he rides the roadways, he calls to any passerby and it is said that if anyone shows that he hears the ghost of Sir Thomas, he too will be carried off to purgatory. 'Tis best to pretend you do not hear.

As with many folktales, there is more than one version of this story and, in one, it is said to be someone else riding in the coach, being driven on a different route.

The Other Blickling Ghosts

Thomas Boleyn was already dead by the time Blickling Hall, as we know it now, was built in 1620 It is quite possible that his ghost haunts the area but, if so, his would not be the only spectral presence!

Some say that his daughter, Anne, rides through Blickling in a coach on the anniversary of her death. This coachman and horses are headless too, and Anne has her head on her lap.

There is a sweet smelling ghost at Blickling too, which is detected by the mysterious lingering aroma of violets. This is said to be the spirit of the wife of the 2nd Earl of Buckinghamshire, a country loving lady who enjoyed making her own perfume out of wild violets from the grounds.

FLIGHT OF THE DRAGONS

On an old parchment, safe in the enclaves of Canterbury Cathedral, is the story of a very strange happening in the ancient county of Suffolk. Told in great detail, and substantiated by date, we can only wonder about what seems to have happened in Little Cornard, on the Essex-Suffolk border. Was it legend, or was it history?

On the afternoon of Friday, September 26th, 1449, the villagers of Little Cornard were alarmed by strange roaring noises coming from the water meadows. Heads lifted in the mud-walled, thatched cottages and men stood still in the fields, all senses tuned in to the growing growling sounds. Children ran crying to their homes for never before, in these days before machinery, had a noise like this been heard.

People began to gather in little clusters, then the boldest amongst them, armed with spears, staffs and one old sword, led a foray across the fields and through the strip of willows and alders that skirted the water meadows. Almost everyone in the village headed riverwards, almost afraid to be left behind. Creeping through the undergrowth, low in the reeds, they peeped out at a fearsome sight.

In the far corner, down where the river curved, was a huge beast, reddish and spotted with dark brown, with a long writhing forked tail, scaly all over and with a horny crest along its back, widening over its head to form ears. The head, redder than the rest of the body, was snoutlike with wide flaring nostrils. Every so often it opened its mouth and roared - an earth rumbling roar that carried for miles.

Suddenly, a hiss from nearby made the villagers' hearts miss beats. When they dared to look again, they could hardly believe their eyes. Not twenty yards away stood another monster, all shiny black, with scales covering its enormous, flabby, low lying body and long smooth tail. It had six strange little legs that moved in a peculiar way and a loathsome, smooth, flat head with a mouth that housed three rows of large, inward pointing teeth.

After posturing for a while, the two beasts advanced, one prancing on strong mobile legs, the other inching forwards in a slithering roll.

The villagers looked on, mesmerised by the horrible scene, as the two dragons, for that is what they were, drew closer together with their posturing growing more grotesque. The hissing and roaring intensified and a billow of flame and smoke shot from the nostrils of the red dragon.

Snarling and hissing in response, the black beast slithered backwards before bending its sinewy neck to make an open-mouthed swipe at the red one. More smoke and flame gushed forth as the red dragon snapped at the black dragon's tail, seizing it in its teeth. The black one hissed and dragged its tail, lunging at the red beast with snapping jaws. It tried to roll on to the agile red one, but it just danced around, still with the tail between its teeth. A green, evil-smelling slime issued from the wound and the red dragon let go amidst a stream of fire. Taking advantage of the red dragon's consternation, the black one seized the other one's crest between its teeth and lifted his opponent from the ground! Shooting flame in his face persuaded him to let go, then the red dragon leapt at the black one's throat. He had to skip backwards out of the way as the black one surged forward, threatening to bury the red dragon under its rolling flab.

For over an hour they tussled and parried, fought and struggled, gaining advantage then losing it. Claw marks and teeth marks in each were growing in number; green slime and red blood flowed on to the trampled grass and soft earth below them. Gradually the roars and hisses diminished and the lunging became lumbering and, eventually, they moved apart to regain breath.

The villagers had watched with silent and bated breath, but suddenly, as if by mutual consent, the animals ceased their fighting and lumbered off with moans and snarls: the Suffolk black dragon to Kedlington Hill and the Essex red dragon to Ballingdon Hill, just south of the River Stour.

The Suffolk folk were amazed by the spectacle they had witnessed and babbled about it amongst themselves and to anyone they met. One of them later told the chronicler, who wrote that old document which can still be seen in Canterbury Cathedral today.

THE HEYDON RAMPART

Heydon lies beyond the Air Museum at Duxford, just off the M11. The villages around here are quiet and easy on the eye but an amazing part of the landscape is formed by the great rampart running from Heydon to Fowlmere. The story behind the building of the rampart is both fascinating and true.

The wind whipped up the long blond hair of the Saxon warrior as he strode to the top of the newly erected bank. His clear blue eyes swept the plain before him, seeing the clumps of trees, the clean stretches of grass and scrubland. He nodded with quiet calm as nothing moved except for a knot of primitive cattle about five hundred yards away. The Saxon strode proudly and confidently, looking at the bank which extended in a sharp brown scar for the great extent of three and a half miles. Today would see a continuation of the work on this bank, which was to be topped by sharp wooden stakes. Piles of them stood nearby waiting for the group of men to knock them in.

Gilda, for that was his name, enjoyed the warm breeze of early June, revelling in the blue tinged dawn. He was dressed in a fur jerkin, woollen cloth trousers, skin boots and gaiters, and carried a long wooden spear with a keen iron blade. He glanced back at the huddle of thatched huts within their stockade, noticing the smoke curling lazily up to the sky. In the centre was the longhouse where he, as chief, had first mooted the idea of this long defensive rampart. Next to the longhouse stood another long, low building with a squat round bell tower. Here Morden, the priest, led them in worship of their old Christian God. Their ancestors had settled in this place some five hundred years ago and all there is to be seen now, where the modern Heydon stands, is a small ring of earthworks.

Now their homes were being threatened by waves of invasions from the Vikings who were sweeping in from northern Europe. Fleeing survivors from the settlements to the east brought tales of rape and plunder by these merciless invaders. Gilda and his brave band of villagers, protected by their great rampart, were confident that the Vikings could be repelled. However, he gazed out anxiously over the great plain before him, then hunched his shoulders and strode back to his home where Pinna, his wife, was preparing breakfast.

Three weeks later, with thoughts of harvesting to be done that day in the small fields that they cultivated, Gilda again climbed the rampart, as he had done daily, and looked over the wooden pallisade on top of the five foot bank. His stomach gave a lurch as he saw, in the distance, the sun shining on the weapons of a large group of men about three miles away. He realised that they were heading straight for the provocative rampart which clearly showed that there was something of value there. Gilda saw that here was a band of about three hundred Vikings, making a foray further to the west and south than they had before, and he ran back to the village.

He dashed to the longhouse and grabbed the long horn which hung there. Putting it to his lips he gave three long blasts before hastening into the hut. Soon an excited, worried crowd had gathered with many anxious enquiries. Silencing the gabbling questions with a bellow, Gilda told them in a clear ringing voice what he had seen. Giving orders that the women and children were to hide in the trees about a mile away, Gilda then deployed the men to their positions on the rampart.

With their shields, spears and swords, the men took up their places and looked fearfully over the pallisade. Unused to fighting, these quiet farming folk felt no match for the Viking warriors who could now be clearly seen about five hundred yards away. They had gathered in a square formation and their leader, a tall blond man with great muscles rippling beneath his mail shirt, was heard stridently encouraging his men. Gilda walked behind the rampart, quietly urging his own men to keep to their places and fight bravely.

Whilst the Anglo Saxons behind the pallisade watched with fearful trepidation, the Vikings turned, formed into a wedge-shaped formation, and started to advance with slow treads. The Vikings came onwards, wearing mail shirts and carrying their two-bladed battle axes. At the side of their wedge were men with bows and quivers of arrows. Hardly pausing in their stride, the bowmen loosed a shower of the arrows and immediately reloaded and produced another deadly shower. The eerie whistle of the arrows unleashed agonised screams from the Anglo Saxons as they found their marks. Again and again they were attacked, and the battle sounds tortured the morning air. In the woods behind, the women and children quaked with fear.

The battle was soon over and the pallisade was hardly touched. Not only was it useless against the arrows of the enemy but it may even have drawn attention to the settlement unnecessarily. Yes, there were a few dead amongst the Vikings, but it was the Anglo Saxons who had been routed and torn asunder. They were like lambs to the slaughter. Gilda, though sickened at the thought of the losses, had survived; he signalled to the Viking chief, Mingel, that any resistence was over.

Together they returned to the longhouse and a peace of sorts was drawn up. Ownership of the land was ceded to the Vikings, who also took the best of the widows and some of the wives. A few Vikings stayed behind in the village but the bulk of them left in search of more conquests. They took the best of the food with them too. The dead were gathered and buried together and peace was restored, like the battle, quickly and quite soundly.

In later years, when people wondered at the power of the primitive folk who had constructed the great defensive rampart, the ghosts of great warriors on the raised earth were often spoken of. The discovery, in the 1950s, of a burial pit containing decapitated Saxon soldiers served only to give credibility to the stories that have always circulated hereabouts.

The Shug Monkey

There is abundant proof of Viking settlements in the Cambridge area, particularly around the Gog Magog Hills. In an ancient document, the written words of a minstrel's song tells the tale of the Viking tale-teller, Aelgud, and his pet from a warmer climate, the Shug Monkey. Aelgud was an old and well-travelled man who eventually settled in the area between Cambridge and Balsham. In the evenings the men would settle down around the fire and Aelgud would tell of his travels to distant lands. He had journeyed far south and had wandered for many years, with his companions, seeking the route back to his homeland. They had travelled along great rivers and over blue oceans, to countries and islands of the brightest greenery, of black and brown peoples, and had marvelled at all of their experiences. For proof of his stories he had, often snuggled inside his clothing for warmth, a little monkey. The creature must have missed the warmth of the sun of his homeland and died during one cold East Anglian winter.

It is said that the monkey's spirit wanders in the area still, and many a person has seen the creature that some say is a demon and others a ghost. It is described as a rough coated but shiny black animal with the face and staring eyes of a tortured monkey. Its restless spirit wanders still around the hedgerows near West Wratting and Balsham, possibly seeking its fellow creatures for warmth and love.

THE WILD MAN OF THE SEA

The lonely four-storied stone keep of Orford Castle is all that is left of a once great building that cost Henry II £1400 to build in 1165, whilst he carried on his fight against Hugh Bigod of Framlingham. In its time it has had many strange inmates, but none stranger than the Wild Man of the Sea.

The two fishermen hauled in the net that they had flung into the water some time before, and a fine lot of shining herring and mackerel splashed, wriggling, into their boat. The sun twinkled on the ruffled surface of the sea, shining on the eight fishing boats just off the beach at Orford. They kept an eye on the large black cloud on the horizon to make sure they were not caught in a storm and kept track of the shoal they were chasing.

The seas of the 1230s held many mysteries for them and occasionally a particularly large or exotic fish would be landed. There were tales of mermaids but the Orford men had never seen them: squids or dolphin were the wonders they spoke of catching every now and again.

The empty net was thrown back into the sea again and the fishermen turned to their oars to paddle for some time to fill it. This time the weight of the catch seemed excessive so they shipped oars and prepared to gather it inboard. They pulled and heaved and soon saw that there was something else underneath the haul of fish. The two exchanged glances and redoubled their efforts. With a final heave, there was a rush and a splatter, the boat bobbed and the net fell inboard. And there, glaring at the fishermen, was a man! Yes, a man, with a long beard and long fair hair, absolutely naked!

He stared at them for a second or so with wild eyes, then started struggling in the net with frenzied movements. He looked so dangerous that his captors gave him a blow on the head with an oar hard enough to send him, senseless, to the bottom of the boat.

As they paddled towards the shore, the rowers yelled out to their friends in the other boats. Their words were incomprehensible but the sound of alarm was clear enough: soon all eight boats were beached.

Everyone was shocked at the sight of the catch, but they were sensitive enough to dress him in some of their spare clothes before carrying him further up the beach! However did he come to be in the water and where did he come from?

When he regained consciousness, he soon earned his nickname of "Wild Man of the Sea", for he pulled weird faces at the sixteen men huddled around him, then stood upright and lunged at them with flailing fists. Although surprised, the fishermen had no trouble pinioning his arms and holding him until they had decided what to do.

The Wild Man needed to be kept somewhere secure, they thought, until it was decided what to do with him, so they took him to Bartholomew de Gladville who was the custodian of Orford Castle. He was put into a cell after the Orford people had tried to communicate with him and failed. He certainly looked wild because of his long matted hair and wide staring eyes but the strangest thing about him was his silence.

Over the next few weeks de Gladville spent much time trying to get him to speak but only succeeded in making him go beserk physically. The only food he would eat was raw fish and all he would drink was plain water, both of which were readily available to him. De Gladville tried all kinds of ways to make him speak: gave him the best fish, gave him no fish, allowed him to walk, tethered or guarded, on the beach, kept him in the dark - even allowed him to swim, tethered, in the shallows, but still no sound. Eventually he seemed to settle to his life in the castle and its surrounds, becoming something of an object of curiosity to the local people who fed him well with marine titbits and treated him as if he were a pet.

The wild man had never made any attempt to leave and so he was only very casually guarded. One day though, he walked a little way away from his guard and, without it being noticed, took off his clothes and slipped quietly into the sea. Someone saw all this happen from a distance and said how quickly the silent man swam away, never to be seen again.

Perhaps he became lonely for his own kind, if he was of another kind - we shall never know.

ALLEY NUMBER SEVENTEEN

We consider it to be quite normal to hear stories of ghosts haunting ancient churches, stately homes and dark and eerie woods.
Much more frightening, somehow, are the spirits of the unquiet dead that manifest themselves in the buildings only associated with today.

Basildon is one of the country's newest towns and among its ordered estates of neat modern housing, its shopping malls and fast-food restaurants, we are unlikely to think of shades of the dead.

The Ambassador Bowling Club has been a popular meeting place for the youth of Basildon for many years. There they could chat, relax and play ten pin bowling, passing away their evenings in carefree amusement. The Ambassador, however, had one attraction which was probably unique amongst all the bowling venues in Britain, for this modern building of polished wood and shining metal was most certainly haunted!

For the uninitiated, bowling centres are arranged into alleys, down which a heavy ball is flung to knock over the pins (like skittles) at the far end. At least that is the idea. This requires considerable skill and a certain amount of strength. One evening in the late 1960s an employee at the centre was startled to hear a ball rolling down alley number 17, which he knew was not in use. He turned and immediately saw there was no-one at all at that end of the room. Before his startled gaze, the ball smashed into the pins, sending them tumbling. A fine score .... by a ghost?

No-one took this incident seriously, though, until another evening some time later. All the customers had left at least two hours earlier, the power had been disconnected for an equal length of time, and suddenly the pin setting equipment which replaces them ready for the next barrage of bowls started up of its own accord, setting up alley number .... 17. Now it was obvious that something very strange was happening. From then onwards it was no surprise when both staff and customers began to see a ghostly figure dressed in blue workman's overalls staring down the haunted alley.

You may find it hard to believe in a haunted bowling alley, but the history of the site itself is interesting. Long before Basildon Newtown was even thought of, there was an isolated farm here. Before World War I, a terrible double murder took place at this farm and, since then, some people have considered the spot to be cursed. This view was reinforced when, in 1940, a young man hanged himself here at the farm. It is interesting to speculate whether or not either case has anything to do with the haunting of the bowling alley, but perhaps there is just something mysterious about the very location.

The Other Ghost

Basildon has two known ghosts, the other one being of the more traditional type.

The Church of the Holy Cross is the oldest building in the town, dating back to the 14th Century. The graveyard is said to be the haunt of a monk in dark red robes who sometimes walks across the road and then vanishes. This spectre has been seen many times by local people, but no-one really knows much about who he was in life. One story suggests that he was murdered near the church in the 16th Century.

THE PEDLAR OF SWAFFHAM

On the ends of the pew, just before the alter in Swaffham Church, and again on an old desk in the chancel, are carved the effigies of John Chapman and his dog. John Chapman and his wife, in blue and purple glass, are in the aisle. His commemoration is due to the story of how he gained his wealth and rebuilt the north aisle of the church in the 15th Century.

The market place in Norwich in the 1440s was probably not that different to the way it is now: noisy, crowded, colourful and quite exciting. The goods on sale will differ, of course, and the way people dress, but the atmosphere would have been very similar.

It was here that John Chapman occasionally had a pitch, selling the copper pots and chargeurs that he had brought, on his packhorse, from Swaffham. He always set out from home before sunrise, then stood amongst the pedlars with their brooches of amethyst and garnets, bone combs and burnished silver mirrors, serfs with their eggs and furmage and dark skinned men selling spices such as cloves, sweet canelle and cubebs, jars of mustard from Lombardy and loaves of wastel bread.

After one particular busy day on Norwich market, he packed up his unsold items and went off to find a beer and lodging for the night, as it was far too dangerous to be out on the road after dark in those days. The next morning he set off on his long walk home. This trip followed the pattern of many others: on his return to Swaffham he put his horse out to grass, stored his wares, moaned to his wife about their lack of money, had a meal and went to bed. That night, however, John had a dream that was to affect the rest of his life.

In this dream John found himself listening to a man repeatedly telling him that if he stood on London Bridge he would hear something that would lead to his fortune. So graphic was the dream that the chapman could not forget it. For days it remained uppermost in his mind and gradually, much to the annoyance of his wife, the compulsion to go to London overcame him.

After a week's preparation John set out for London with only his dog, and his backpack of clothes and food. For days and days he travelled, finally arriving in the bustling city and his final destination.

John took up his station at the end of London Bridge and watched the passing population with intent and interested eyes. Some people asked his business and talked with him but he heard nothing that would lead to his fortune.

For two whole days he stood there, just watching and waiting and even the passing hours did not shake his assurance.

Then, on the third day, a man asked him why he stood there. So open and frank was this man's face that John told him it was because of a dream. It turned out that this stranger was also a dreamer, but one who had no fatih in his dreams, for he replied, "Alas my friend, if I believed in dreams, I would be as much a fool as you. Recently I dreamed that if I went to the home of John Chapman, a pedlar who lives in Swaffham in Norfolk, and dug under a tree which grows at the back of his house, I would find a buried pot of treasure." Scarcely able to believe his ears, quickly John took his leave and headed back towards East Anglia.

On reaching his house, he wasted no time at all. A spade was found and the digging began. Mistress Chapman looked on in amazement, after hearing her husband's story, and was flabberghasted when eventually the spade uncovered a box bearing a curious Latin inscription. Opening the box with trembling hands, John found that it was full of money! The pair were delighted, but wondered about the words on the box lid. Keen to find out their meaning, the crafty pedlar put the box in his window and, sure enough, some young men who knew the language soon knocked on the door. They translated the couplet:

Under me doth lie
Another much richer than I

So again John Chapman dug, this time deeper than before, and he found a huge pot brimming over with coins and jewels!

His fortune made, and the peace of his mind restored, the pedlar spent some of his money wisely and became one of the respected local gentry. To thank God for his good fortune, John Chapman paid for the rebuilding of the north aisle of the church and, in their turn, the good people of Swaffham thanked him by weaving him forever into the patchwork of their town's history.

There he remains still, an emblem for the town, as the sign outside Swaffham shows.

MARY JANE
AND THE EXCISE MEN

At Blyford, between Blythburgh and Halesworth on the main A12, is the low-roofed, thatched inn known as the Queen's Head. Its plastered walls are painted cream and its yellow doors are set in green frames. Flower baskets hang from the roof, creating a pleasing panorama. This inn, like many others in Suffolk, was a centre for smuggling.

In the early days of the 19th century the government's revenue and excise forces were strengthened by tough men who had been demobilised after the Napoleonic Wars. Due to the strength and vigilance of these officers, smuggling became a much bigger challenge.

Many of the East Anglian beaches were used to the drama of boats being silently rowed to the shore line, men creeping across the sand to meet the oarsmen and receive the contraband. The Suffolk coast, in particular, was known for this sort of activity, with many locals, fishermen and others, being involved in the extremely lucrative trade of smuggling.

One night a large run of brandy was organised to be collected from the beach at Dunwich, so large that pack-horses and donkeys were required. The kegs of liquor were being carried off towards Dunwich Walks, destined for the Ship Inn, and it was a night for soft whistles, lapping waves and muffled footfalls. Then came the word that the revenue men were out and a ripple of alarm spread through the moonlit string of men and horses. They were used to such warnings and had contingency plans, so soon the haul was diverted through a network of lanes and byways to the Queen's Head at Blyford.

The landlord, John Key, and his wife were aroused from sleep by low whistles and soft tappings at diamond-paned windows. John knew the procedure, having taken part himself in several runs, let the men in and began to direct operations. Soon brandy was being stashed away in a hiding place over the fireplace and more was directed to be hidden in the church across the road, under the alter and pews. Some brandy was even taken to the neighbouring church of Westhall where it was hidden in the valley between the double roof.

At that time, John and Martha Key had a nine-year-old girl called Mary Jane living with them and the child, from behind a chair, watched the furtive but frantic activities of the smuggling band as they hid their booty. All was bustle: the rattling of feet and barrels, the clink of stone bottles, the hoarse, urgent whispers, grey figures and black shadows. Then, as suddenly as it began, the shadowy figures passed back into the dark of the night, the whispering breeze hung in the chimney and the members of the household wondered what to do next. The clock ticked on and on, as they waited for something to happen. They knew the excise men would arrive, and felt that they ought to take extra precautions, so Mary Jane was taken up to the bedroom and all her clothes were removed. Martha rubbed the girl's chest and arms with turpentine and mustard, to inflame the skin and make it very red. Meanwhile, in the kitchen, John was boiling kettles and pouring the hot water into four hot water bottles which were wrapped in pieces of old blanket. Mary Jane was put into her truckle bed and the hot bottles were placed around her. Just imagine how she felt!

Within thirty minutes, galloping horses were heard and there was a knocking at the door so fierce that it opened before John could reach it. In stumbled four customs and excise men, smart in clean-cut uniforms, with their complexions rosy from their exertions. Their heavy boots clattered on the quarry tiles and the sharp voice of the officer in charge rang out, demanding to search the house. Martha bade them enter but asked them to be quiet for there was scarlet fever in the house. The officer and his men shuffled, for in those days scarlet fever was a contagious killer.

"Do come and see the child for yourself," Martha invited the officer when he questioned the truth of the statement. He followed her upstairs where Mary Jane's condition was all too evident. Before he and his men hastily left the house the officer pressed a florin into Martha's hand with best wishes for Mary Jane's recovery.

Mary Jane 'survived' the fever and, when she was twelve, went into service at the big house at Westleton. Here she met Sam Edwards, a young horseman who was employed nearby, and became involved in smuggling once more. For Sam had found that smuggling was much more exciting and lucrative than his regular job and eventually they were able to take over the Duke of Marlborough public house at Weston,near Beccles, continuing their smuggling for the rest of Sam's life.

Dunwich: A Lost City

For all we know, Dunwich may still be used by smugglers, but it is now best known as a beauty spot and for the ghostly sounds of underwater church bells. The heath is maintained by the National Trust and there are delightful woodland walks close to the picturesque village.

Village it may be now, but once Dunwich was a very important city with huge gates of brass, a bustling harbour, many churches and hospitals, a king's palace and a mint.

There is evidence that the Ancient Britons settled in the great forests along the coast here, then the Romans established a stronghold, known as Sitomagus, on the site of the original ancient Dunwich. After the Romans withdrew in the fifth century, the Jutes, Saxons and Angles followed, eventually making Dunwich the capital city of East Anglia, because of its valuable harbour. Then came the fiery Danes and Dunwich was sacked, but the Normans rebuilt the port and within 150 years it became a rich and prosperous place once more. Even then, though, the sea was beginning to encroach upon the forests on either side of Dunwich.

In 1351 a huge spit of sand built up across the harbour, preventing craft entering or leaving the port. Although gaps were cut in the spit, they silted up rapidly and from then onwards the importance of Dunwich decreased. The dissolution of the monasteries exacerbated the situation for so many of the town's major buildings began to fall into decay.

Great storms between 1680 and 1740 wreaked havoc in the town, washing away whole streets at once. In 1919 the last church of Dunwich, All Saints, disappeared over the cliffs, leaving just James Street. Visitors today can visit the museum there, then stroll along the grassy sunken track through Greyfriars Wood: it is said that the birds never sing here.

Cities don't have ghosts, do they?

THE GRANTCHESTER TUNNELS

Grantchester is one of the loveliest villages in Cambridgeshire and is famous for its links with Rupert Brooke, who had rooms in the Old Vicarage during his Cambridge undergraduate days. It is also known for an intriguing mystery which has never been solved.

Each year the Royston June Fair was held where the Icknield Way crossed Ermine Street and this year, 1724, was no different.

Robert Ling had enjoyed the Fair, as usual, because the people of Royston had enjoyed his violin playing and had shown their appreciation by throwing money into his hat. Under the maple tree on The Green, the crowds had lounged in the sun, quite beguiled by his music, but now it was time to move on.

The Cambridge Fair was next and so Robert followed his usual route through Melbourne, Foxton, Harston and to Trumpington where, sore of foot, he stayed the night at the Three Horse Shoes Inn. The next morning he turned off the main road and headed towards Grantchester, partly because it was a beautiful road but also because it provided a short cut to the north west of the city where the fair was to be held that year.

Robert strode through the countryside, admiring the scenery and watching the working men, women and children in the fields, pulling weeds from the corn, tending the animals, leading the oxen through their arduous paces. There were few travellers around as this was not a main road, but even the solitude was pleasant.

On arrival at Grantchester, the musician stopped at a hostelry and purchased a pint of good foaming ale and some fresh bread and cheese, settling back to enjoy a relaxing break. So relaxing, in fact, that he decided to stay there for three nights instead of walking on to Cambridge where the inkeepers would have hoisted their lodging charges because of the Fair. The Grantchester innkeeper was happy to accept Robert's offer to play his fiddle in the evenings in exchange for a reduction in his bed and board charges. Both benefited from this arrangement financially as the inn's customers, both regulars and travellers, were appreciative.

Amongst the visitors was a team of travelling builders who were employed at Grantchester Manor, relaying the worn flagged floor in the kitchen. As the large old tiles had been raised the sandy floor had been revealed and the builders had been excited to find a bricked opening in the corner. Steps that seemed to have been untrodden for years led down to what appeared to be a cellar. One of the men had gone down with a handful of burning straw and was surprised to find a bricked tunnel leading away into the pitch black darkness. None of the builders had dared to go any further but, as they sat listening to the clear notes of the violin that evening in the inn, they hatched out a plan.

The fiddler was to be offered a sovereign to go down the tunnel, playing his violin. They would follow the sound above the ground and in that way find out where the tunnel went to. The idea amused Robert Ling and so it was that, next morning at 10 o'clock, he arrived at the Manor. Mr and Mrs Lansdowne, the owners, their steward, Mr Parker, and the three builders were all waiting for him, quite excited about solving the mystery.

Making his way through the manor house, Robert marvelled at the grandeur of the deep carpets, the huge dark paintings, pannelled walls and heavy brocade hangings. Emerging into the kitchen, with its wide sandy floor, bare walls and lack of furniture, Robert's eyes were immediately drawn to the hole in the ground. Nearby was a candle which was lit by a taper; he picked it up, held it in his left hand and stood on the first step. After a few words with the others, he drew the bow over the taut strings. Not a tremor of wind or sound affected the tapering candle flame.

With cries of good luck ringing in his ears, Robert descended the steps and entered the tunnel. The clear strong notes of the violin were clearly heard on the still morning air as the group of listeners hurried outside into the herb garden. They stilled their tongues and followed the music, which became more and more faint, through the gate and into the orchard. The notes were difficult to hear by now, and eventually became completely lost in the gentle soughing breeze which rustled the apple boughs.

With baited breath they waited, and waited, and waited for the sound to be caught again, but only the birds and the breeze could be heard. With some anxiety, and ever quickening steps, they returned to the kitchen. Near to the tunnel mouth no sound could be heard and nothing could be seen either; no sign of the candlelight they had hoped for.

The three builders and their employers stood motionless, straining all of their senses in hope, but only stillness crept out of the tunnel. Not one of them dared to go down the stairs to look, and each of them had to look to their consciences and live with their nightmares.

Poor Robert Ling has no marked last resting place: indeed, according to some white-haired old gentlemen of Grantchester, his spirit wanders still. The tunnel is still there, somewhere, keeping safely its dreadful secret.

The Go Between

In medieval Cambridge much use was made of secret tunnels between colleges and buildings belonging to the religious orders. There is one between the buildings that are now Jesus College and Abbey House on Newmarket Road.

Jesus College was once St Radegund's Nunnery and here, in 1154, lived Sister Benedict, a beauiful lady with a sad history.

She was the grand-daughter of a nobleman who had lost both life and land at Battle near Hastings, in 1066. Her family had to take flight and the young girl was put in the care of the nuns in Cambridge, where vows of silence and chastity were enforced. As Sister Benedict grew up, she found it difficult to maintain her vows and eventually fell in love with a monk from a nearby Augustinian priory. It was extremely awkward for the pair to meet and so a go-between was used, a young child dressed in a fur jacket and hood. This child used the tunnel between St Radegund's and the priory to deliver messages but after some time he informed on the couple. The lovers were excommunicated and the child had to live in the streets.

It was a very long, cold winter and the go-between died, but his spirit delivers messages along the tunnel to Abbey House still. Some have seen a long furry penguin-like creature, with an evil, cloying presence - and a guilty conscience!

THE GREEN MAN

The legend of the Green Man of Norwich is like the green man himself: too indefinite to be called a memory and too factual to be called a superstition. You can see his portrait on the Wild Man Inn sign in Bedford Street and on the Green Man sign at Rackheath on the main Norwich to Stalham road. He seems to have existed, but what were his origins?

Once upon a long time ago, Danu, the last of the green men, lived in the woods just to the south east of the present day Norwich. He was small, dressed all in green and had a sharp pointed nose and ears to match. His home was among the trees down by the water, and he was very familiar with the quiet trodden ways, the sheltered sunny dells and the shady pools where the fish were easy to catch. Danu spent most of his time in the woods but sometimes went into Norwich, flitting in and out of the nooks and crannies of the town, gaining vast amusement by watching the antics of the human folk there. Some people swore that they saw him, but only out of the corners of their eyes: once they turned to look, he vanished. His wild face and green suit was spotted often enough, however, to convince people of his presence.

One day Danu was enjoying himself in King Street, sitting unseen on ledges, peeping from behind a chimney stack, glancing through a slightly open door, hiding in a shadowed corner of a wall. He was having a fine time among the merchants' houses. Suddenly he heard the sound of crying and, peering over the bedroom window ledge of one of the homes, he saw a young girl weeping bitterly.

"What shall I do?" the girl sobbed. "How can I get out of

marrying that horrible man?"

Unable to contain his curiosity, Danu jumped through the open window and sat on the sill, frightening the girl, who made to hide behind the curtains of her bed. Danu cried out, "Do not be afraid. Tell me your troubles and let me see if I can help you."

The sobbing slowly subsided and soon she was telling her story to Danu. Her name was Alizon and she was the eldest daughter of Simon Walpole, a greedy merchant who wanted to increase his riches by marrying his daughter off to Philip Crump. Not only was Crump twenty years older than Alizon, he was miserly and miserable too. "Oh, he is horrible," she sobbed anew, "and I will do anything to get out of it, but my father's mind is made up and there is no escape for me. I have to stay locked in my room until the wedding and that is to be on Saturday. Oh, what can I do?"

Danu thought how lovely she looked as Alizon put her head to her pillow and wept tears which clung to her beautiful lashes before trickling down her cheeks. "Anything? Will you do anything?"

"Anything," she cried. "Yes, I would do anything rather than condemn myself to a life with him."

"Then this is what you must do," replied Danu. "I will come back again on Friday evening at 8 o'clock and if, by then, you have guessed my name you will go free and will not have to marry Philip Crump. But if you have not guessed my name, then you will have to come and live with me."

Alizon looked at Danu and did not know which would be worse, for that little wild green man would never be a husband to her. But Crump? No, never. "All right," she said, thoughtfully, "I agree."

Danu leapt through the window and although Alizon jumped up straight away, she did not see the little figure scampering off into the shadows and across Conisford Bridge.

Calling in her servant, Matilda, Alizon breathlessly told her of the encounter with the little green man. Matilda thought that the forthcoming marriage had deprived Alizon of her senses, but she did as she was told and sought out John Prior, Alizon's lover, and told him the story and asked him to find the information that was needed.

John did not know where to look or who to ask first, but he visited the inns and hostelries of the town asking his questions, telling of his mission, being laughed at and told to go to Babel. Through the streets John wandered all day Wednesday and then Thursday too. By midnight on Thursday he had begun to despair and gloomily he headed out of the city and on to the marshes.

Out here the last hours of the night were alive with the sounds of the marsh: the scurrying of voles, the rustling of mice, the croaking of frogs, the whirring of owls and the whisk and whine of the breeze as it whispered through the rushes and bushes. John wandered on and on and as first light crept over the eastern sky, he thought he saw a light flickering in the trees. His steps took him towards it and, from his hiding place in the bushes, he saw a little green man dancing around a fire and singing as he danced:

I will have you, my lovely girl
To be my bride so true.
I'll give you no clue, my lovely girl,
My name: it just grew and grew.
Your gamble you will rue, my lovely girl
For you'll never guess my name: Danu!

John heard and, with mighty relief, he headed back to Norwich. His search had exhausted him and it would be well to gain some sleep before he went to tell Alizon the news.

And so he fell asleep and was aghast, when he woke, to find

that it was 25 minutes before 8 o'clock and he had half a mile to run to get to Alizon's house! On arrival he summoned the maid, Matilda, and quickly told her what he had heard. Matilda wrote the name on a small piece of paper, put it under a glass of wine on a plate and hurried up the stairs to her mistress's room.

Danu was already there and, hearing the knock on the door, ran behind the curtain. Matilda entered and saw that Alizon had been weeping. She smiled as she put down the plate with the glass of wine and pointed to the paper.

After the maid had left, Danu came round the curtain and taunted Alizon, saying that she would never guess his name and that soon she would be in the woods with him. Alizon spoke quietly to him: "I will keep my promise and you will keep yours, Danu."

With a shriek of rage, Danu fled, but made a full recovery and was soon seen again, out of the corners of people's eyes only, in many a shady place.

All Alizon had to do was wait for the next day and see what happened. It was a long night but, at 11 o'clock in the morning, news came that Philip Crump had been killed when an oak treee had fallen on his carriage in Shotesham. This left Alizon free to marry John Prior and they both lived happily ever after.

The Green Children of the Tunnels

Danu is not the only 'green' person in East Anglian folklore. Many years ago some villagers from the Suffolk village of Woolpit St Mary found a young brother and sister who had white hair and green skin. At first the village folk were scared of them, quite naturally, but the young ones were upset and confused, and spoke in a foreign tongue. Later, when able to communicate, the girl said that they came from a faraway land and had become lost in some tunnels, which eventually came out into the disused clay pits in Suffolk! The villagers used to throw captured wolves into the pits and leave them there to die - hence the corrupted name of the village.

The green children seemed to have existed on a diet of green vegetables and fruit, which probably affected the colour of their skin, and could not adapt to the local diet easily.

The boy died that winter, but his sister survived, gradually adapting to her surroundings and diet. Her skin eventually lost its pale green hue and her hair darkened. She grew to be a very beautiful lady and apparently married someone from Kings Lynn, then lived to a contented old age.

THE CUBE CHURCH

Many people travelling along the holiday waters in the Beccles area have had their attention caught by the sight of the curious church tower at Burgh St Peter. It has the appearance of a tower of toy bricks, getting smaller and smaller, which have been piled up by a child. Attached to this is the thatched body of the church, 100 ft long and 14 ft wide. It is a good place to avoid during the evening and night time of May 2nd.

Adam Morland owned a poor farm in Burgh St Peter way back in Saxon times. There was a Roman castle standing proudly nearby, although it had previously been ransacked by the feuding Saxons and Angles, before they settled peacefully on the land.

Adam's house had a roof of thatch, walls made from wood and mud and stood on a shallow rise on the marshes. Gaining a living from the land was extremely difficult and of eight children born only three survived infancy. Whatever the weather and state of the harvest, the tithes and tributes still had to be paid before Adam could think of possibly increasing his stock.

One particular winter was extremely hard: Adam's youngest child died of a fever and his wife, too, was very ill. During the long nights of worry Adam wondered whether to leave his farm and try to earn a living elsewhere.

At last the spring sun began to warm the ground of the marshes and Adam considered that his wife was well enough to be left to fend for herself. So, towards the end of April, Adam left his farm and set out on his search for work, or something which would help his family survive.

His wanderings led him by St John's Priory where he saw the monks going to and fro, happy and singing in their work. One monk listened to the sad story the farmer had to tell but Adam felt that he could offer him no more assistance than a special prayer. He sank down onto a fallen willow trunk and held his head in his hands but looked up when he heard soft footsteps, which paused, and saw that an elderly monk had sat down beside him. He had a tired but kindly voice and encouraged Adam to tell his tale again, listening sympathetically. Then, from a purse tied to a string around his waist, the old man drew ten gold coins and pressed them into Adam's hand. In those days this represented a large but not a princely sum. Adam protested but the old man said that all he wanted was Adam's thumbprint in a block of wax that he had, then repayment in ten years time.

Unable to believe his good fortune, Adam gladly pressed his thumb into the wax and agreed to an arrangement for full repayment a decade hence. As soon as he had done this, though, the old man threw off his cloak and cowl and dashed off up the road! Aghast at the very thought, Adam saw that his 'benefactor' had assumed the form of the devil and realised that he had just sold him his soul.

With an extremely heavy heart, Adam turned homewards and wondered how he could possibly explain his actions to his sensible wife.

Seeing his grief and sincerity, even though she found his story very difficult to understand or believe, Adam's wife had a few suggestions to make about what they should do with the gold coins. They decided, after talking well into the night, that Adam would use just part of the money to improve the farm so that their income would increase. The rest of the gold would be used to buy materials to build a small church on the same site as the one standing there today.

Over the next years Adam toiled relentlessly on his farm to earn the money to buy back his soul and, in his spare time, with the help of some good friends, worked on the church building.

The time for repayment came closer and Adam, exhausted by his efforts on both farm and church, died just three days before the date on which he was to repay the gold or give his soul to the devil. He did not rest in peace.

If you are in the area of Burgh St Peter on the second day of May, it would be wise to avoid the churchyard. If you did not heed this advice, however, you may see the spirit of an old man there, his clothes covering nothing but a skeleton with the fires of Hell burning inside it. Beware!

YAXLEY MILL

Between Whittlesey and Benwick , in Cambridgeshire,
there used to lay a great stretch of water
known as Whittlesey Mere. It was drained in 1851
but until then it covered nearly 2000 acres.
The mere was well known for the great
storm that turned its surface to a rage of white foam.

By the side of Whittlesey Mere stood Yaxley stone mill, a mill of great antiquity, with a stone base and a wooden cap. On some stonework in the basement was said to be the inscription 'MW 1671'. Sadly, the mill was demolished in 1965 but the workmen could not remove the spirit that has haunted the site for years. In the past it was considered that Yaxley Stone Mill, Glatton Round Mill and Whittlesey Mere were the three wonders of Huntingdonshire. Not one of these wonders exist now and neither, of course, does Huntingdonshire.

It was late in the 1530s and Henry VIII's commissioners were abroad, desecrating and despoiling the holy houses of the land. They came to the abbey at Sawtry, a small monastic foundation where the monks prayed, and carried out their ministerial duties, amongst the early medieval farmlands and woodlands just west of the fens. Unlike neighbouring Ramsey Abbey, it was not a rich place but pilgrims on their journeys were glad of the rest and peace that this abbey afforded them. Amongst its few humble treasures was the chalice, a beautiful, delicate vessel which had come to this country from France, a gift of a band of pilgrims.

Abbot Thomas cared for and loved his abbey very much and his heart was broken when news of the despoilers' arrival reached him. Dr Legh was the commissary in charge of the party charged with organising the destruction of this East Anglian abbey, and others. He was successful in persuading half of the monks to give up their vows and leave, but Abbot Thomas stayed, begging for his abbey to be left alone. His pleas fell on deaf ears for the men had already started their demolition work.

In similar circumstances, Abbot John Lawrence of Ramsey was to give in to the commissioners, accepting a handsome pension and going to live in his grand house at Bodsey. All of his monks were dispersed and well provided for.

Abbot Thomas of Sawtry beseeched one of the vile commissioners, Ivan Throgmorton, to at least leave him the chalice as it was of little value. In reply, Throgmorton took the delicate vessel in his hand, feigning to cherish it, but then he flung it to the ground in a spot where masonry was falling. With a cry of pain, Abbot Thomas flung himself upon the cup as if to protect it. Tumbling stones fell upon him and he died there in what must have been an agony of both mind and body.

The site of the Sawtry Abbey is still traceable, with ditches, excavations and fishponds marking the site. Some of the materials from the abbey are in All Saints Church at Sawtry but most of the masonry was sold at the time of destruction to a man who subsequently used them to build the great Black Stone Mill at Yaxley. It is the site of the now demolished Yaxley Mill that is still haunted by the spirit of old Abbot Thomas, who cannot rest until the stones of Sawtry are replaced and he can hold the chalice in his hands once more.

The incense boat from Ramsey Abbey, found in Whittlesey Mere.

Treasures of Whittlesey Mere

After Henry VIII split from the Papal Church the desecration and destruction of the monasteries began. In Cambridgeshire, all but Peterborough were affected.

At Ramsey Abbey, the abbot and his monks were paid off and dispersed, and the site sold to Richard Cromwell. In a frantic atttempt to save something from the abbey, someone threw two of its finest pieces of silver into Whittlesey Mere. For over 300 years they lay there, the censer in which incense was burnt during high mass, and the exquisite incense boat decorated with a rams head at either end.

The Mere was drained in 1850 and, after the water disappeared, local people fixed boards to their feet, to prevent sinking, and went on a curiosity hunt. Joseph Coles, only 17 years old, found the censer from Ramsey Abbey as well as a few other items. Joseph realised that he had something special but thought it was an ancient lamp. He took it home and washed it carefully, then he had the metal tested and found that it was made of solid silver and washed with gold. The Lord of the Manor, Mr Wells, as owner of the land laid claim to the treasure and paid the boy £25 for it. In turn, he sold it Lord Carysfoot of Elton Hall for £1,100.

The incense boat was lying near the censer and was found by someone hunting near to Joseph Cole; both saw it and thought it was an ornamental snuff box. This treasure of Ramsey Abbey was sold to Lord Carysfoot as well, and graced Elton Hall for some time.

These two items of monastic silver are now safely housed in the Victoria and Albert Museum and represent some of finest illustrations of mediaeval workmanship to survive the dissolution of the monastries and escape destruction.

THE WATCHMEN WATCHED

Oil refineries at night, from a distance, can look eerily beautiful - a bit like a science fiction wonderland. The Mobil Oil Corporation at Coryton, near Southend in Essex, has its own special eerie moments.

At 8pm one cold December night, George was on duty long after his colleagues had left. The great metal oil tanks and pipelines lend the complex a modern, even futuristic, feel and ghosts of the past were far from George's mind. Most pressing was the need to get out of the cold wind, so he climbed into the cab of an oil tanker.

Having settled himself comfortably into the silence, George was surprised to hear footsteps coming down the road towards him. Surprised, because he knew he was supposed to be alone in the plant, but pleased at the prospect of having some company to dispel the boredom of his lonely night's watch. George leaned out of the cab and bellowed a cheerful "Hello!".

The sound of footsteps continued but there was no reply. Soon, through the darkness, he made out the shape of the mysterious intruder who was still walking towards him, now about twenty feet away. The man was not tall but he certainly was quite hefty and, for the first time, George felt a thrill of apprehensive fear. Who was this stranger? Why did he not speak?

"Who is it?" he shouted, but the man, who he now saw to be dressed in blue overalls and a white steel safety helmet, continued to advance. George was a brave man and he knew that he had to challenge the trespasser. He ran towards him, shouting, but as he reached his target ..... he was gone. Vanished without a trace. Very shaken, George called up Security and also wrote a report for his boss: but they knew the story already.

Yes, the site was haunted, he was told, and had been since the 1950s when the site was owned by Cory Brothers, fuel distributors. One of their nightwatchmen had slipped and fallen into the separator tank, a machine which cleans the oil from the effluent. He had drowned in the disgusting oily dregs and, ever since then, his ghostly remains have been glimpsed by certain receptive workers at the plant.

Other Modern Phenomena

George was understandably frightened when he came across his ghost in the oil refinery, but imagine how revellers at a Butlin's Holiday Camp would feel if they were joined by a visitor from the past.

Clacton-on-Sea is still a popular holiday resort and for many years there was a Butlins Camp there, with its famous "Good Morning Campers" wake up calls. Sadly, the fashion changed and cut price holidays abroad made the site unprofitable so it closed down. The grand ballroom still remains, however, and so quite possibly does the ghost of a soldier killed in an off duty drunken brawl there many years ago!

One of the UKs most dramatic UFO stories comes from near Sudbury, on the Suffolk/Essex border. A young couple were driving in this area late one night when the engine of their car stalled. They both got out, examined the engine, and then continued driving to their destination. On arrival, they were shocked to discover that it was 1.30 in the morning - they had lost three hours! Under hypnosis by an expert from the East Anglian UFO & Paranormal Research Association, a familiar story emerged from the woman witness. She claimed to have entered a flying saucer whilst her husband was placed in suspended animation. Later she was returned safely and their journey continued. True story? Or could it be similar to other cases of False Memory Syndrome widely reported in the press.

BLACK TOBY OF BLYTHBURGH

In the middle of the 1700s the British Army was involved in fighting the War of the Austrian Succession. After the battle at Dettingen, the regiment led by Sir Robert Rich came to Blythburgh in Suffolk for a period of rest and renewal. Their uniformed arrival provided quite a spectacle and much excitement amongst the local folk, but one soldier in particular caught the eyes and imagination of the girls: Tobias Gill. This drummer was a tall, strapping Negro who wielded his drumsticks with great panache.

Once the regiment had set up camp and settled in, the soldiers began to mix with the local population. Soon tales of their exploits circulated, including some that must have been exaggerated. There were romantic entanglements and drunken brawls in the public houses and many of the tales involved Tobias Gill, or Black Toby as he was known. He was immensely strong and liked to drink a great deal.

The problem was that Black Toby could not take his drink well and became easily agitated and angry. Often he would strike out with his mighty fists, leaving some poor man nursing a bruised or broken jaw. The other soldiers kept away from Toby as much as possible, not because of the the colour of his skin, for this much-travelled regiment had fought in many lands and had come to know that a man's race or colour had no relation to his worth. No, they just preferred not to be involved in any trouble he may cause. Several times he was reported for his misdemeanors and dealt with harshly. For weeks at a time he would be confined to camp and, during that time, would be a model soldier because there was no alcohol available. His weeks of punishment would end, though, and he would soon find himself in trouble again.

The young ladies certainly found him fascinating for, when sober, he had a charm and magnetism which attracted them. Most of them learned, however, that a night out with Black Toby was not the delight that they had been led to expect. Many fathers banned their daughters from keeping his company, quite wisely.

Before too long, Toby had become so unpopular in Blythburgh that he had to go public houses further afield. He started to frequent the ale houses of Walberswick, several miles away, and one summer evening, on his walk back to camp, he met Ann Blakemore walking across the common. Toby greeted her but this serving girl had been out with him before and tried to ignore him. Because he had had too much to drink, Toby was displeased and tried to force Ann to spend some time with him. Apparently she panicked and ran away from him. With his brain fuddled by drink, Toby chased after Ann and caught her by the flying ends of the kerchief around her neck. No-one knows exactly what happened next, but the result of this chance meeting was that Ann died after struggling to escape from his clutches, and Toby lay in a drunken stupor in the grass at the side of her body.

Next morning, soon after dawn, some labourers on their way to work came upon the scene and fetched the local constable. Toby was still drunk and could remember nothing. He was taken to the gaol at Bury St Edmunds to await trial, charged with the rape and murder of Ann Blakemore.

Tobias Gill was found guilty and received a death sentence. He was hanged on a rough gallows and then his body was taken to the spot on the common where he had killed Ann and placed in a gibbet. Gibbets are horrible things, metal cages, almost, in which a body is placed and left indefinitely. The wind and beasts of both sky and earth are allowed to do their worst.

Black Toby's death was an awful one and it is not at all surprising that his spirit stays in Blythburgh, haunting the heathland where his crime was committed. The path across this common land is known as Toby's Walks and the whole area can feel decidedly spooky still!

Spirits of Blythburgh

Black Toby is just one of many spectral visitors to Blythburgh. A number of the larger buildings are haunted by monks, and spirits of witches burnt at the stake remain at Dead Man's Corner.

The ubiquitous East Anglian Black Shuck has been seen on the common and in the church and, as the story behind this big black dog differs from the others considerably, is worth telling here. This dog was said to be the Devil incarnate.

On August 14, 1577, the priest was addressing his flock in the Holy Trinity Church. At this time the church was barely a hundred years old, a beautiful many windowed building with a massive tower. As the droning continued from the pulpit, words about the Devil, brimstone, fire and Hell, and no doubt some of paradise and Heaven too, the parishioners noticed that the sound of the wind around the church and its tower was getting louder. When it reached screaming pitch the priest stopped talking and watched, in shock, as the spire fell through the tower roof and onto the floor of the church! Great lumps of masonry fell from the tower smashing the beautiful carved font to bits. Worse still, it crashed onto a group of people seated on rushes near the font, killing two of them outright and another lady died later.

Swirls of dust caused coughing, choking and streaming eyes but through this a great black dog, with red eyes and long legs, was seen to fall with the stones from the roof.

This creature from Hell gave off a searing heat and scorched anyone it neared. It rampaged through the church, clawing at the door to get out, then disappeared out towards Bungay, taking the noisy tempest with him. Many people cowered in the church for some time, suffering from shock, and the claw marks that remained on the door convinced them that they had indeed been visited by the Devil.

BLACK SHUCK

Stories of spectral black dogs are quite common
in East Anglia, especially along the coastline.
On the North Norfolk coast, their apparition is known
as Old Shuck, or Black Shuck, a name derived from the
Anglo Saxon word 'soucca' meaning demon.
This is the story of the origin of the Norfolk Shuck
story, as told by local men who claim to know the truth.

The night of January 28th, 1709, was one of the type dreaded by the seafarers who had to sail their craft through Devil's Throat. This is a temperamental stretch of sea off the north easterly corner of Norfolk, between Blakeney and Mundesley. On this night, waves of over twenty feet high rose white and murderous, lashed by the howling gale that tore at the sea with destructive force. The storm rushed, with torrents of water, onto the beaches and across the marshes. Trees, houses and churches were damaged and the cottagers prayed to God for deliverance: some of the more hard-hearted ones also looked forward to the pickings of a shipwreck!

And shipwreck there was that night, on the beach of Salthouse. In the early hours of the morning the brig 'Ever Hopeful', from Whitby, had been caught by the storm whilst returning to Yorkshire from London, loaded with a cargo of fruit, spices and other foodstuffs. The captain and crew tried to manoeuvre their small craft in the screaming wind but they were carried helplessly towards the shallow shoals off the coast. There were flickering beacons on the top of the church towers at Cromer and Blakeney but the rest of the seashore was unlit. On such a night these lights were not helpful.

The ship gave a lurch and the inevitable timber tearing sound was heard above the howling wind as she grounded on a bank off Salthouse. The pounding waves soon broke up the craft, causing spars, doors and rails to be whirled aloft. The screams of the doomed crew added to the horrendous atmosphere and one by one they lost their hold on the disintegrating ship. The captain, seeing that to stay would be but to delay death, resolved to make a desperate bid for life. Seizing his pet wolf-hound by the collar, he jumped clear of the ship and into the turbulent waves. They struck out for the shore, only tens of yards away, but were overcome by the currents and drowned.

In the quiet morning air, the locals were combing the beach for valuables when they came across the bodies of both man and dog. The captain was still grasping the dog's collar, and the dog's jaws were tightly clamped to his master's reefer jacket, clearly telling how man and dog had clung to each other in their desperation. There were no survivors at all and the bodies of the crew and the captain were taken to Salthouse churchyard and buried in unmarked graves. A hole was dug in the sandy beach and the big black wolfhound was buried there.

Within a few weeks, people had seen a large black dog running backwards and forwards along the beach between Cley and Salthouse, and heard it howling for its master. As the years have passed his legendary appearance has become more grotesque, and the most recent sightings have him the size of a calf, with large red eyes and a shaggy coat as black as ebony.

People have felt the hound padding behind them but no-one sensible would turn to look: would they live to tell the tale? No one in their right mind would even consider roaming the marshes between Salthouse and Cley at night, expecially in late January, or whenever the sea is lashed by storms!

WICKHAMPTON HEARTS

In the ancient church at Wickhampton there is a stone effigy of Sir William Gerbygge with his wife at his side and a lion at his feet. He wears a flowing tunic over his armour, carries a sword and shield and, curiously, is holding a stone heart in his hand. That heart is involved in a strange and macabre story.

During the reign of Edward I, about the turn of the 12th Century, the marshy land around Breydon Water was owned by Sir Valence Gerbygge. There were two villages here and for simplicity's sake we will use their present day names. Wickhampton had one large farm near the church and good hunting grounds and Halvergate, the better of the two, had rich arable land, many fine farms and a noble church.

Sir Valence managed the estate, and all who lived on it, with his two sons, Gilbert, the elder, and William. The farmland was rich and crops were plentiful. Animal husbandry was profitable for the damp pastures yielded lush grazing in the summer and abundant crops of hay for winter months. There was ample building material from the timbers in the woods and the muddy clay from the marshes. Wild life abounded, making hunting a sporting certainty and providing cheap food for everyone. Life should have been good but the young men both had extremely quarrelsome and jealous natures and often had to be reproached by their father.

Gilbert and William regularly argued over their eventual inheritance and this was a source of worry to their father. However, as was the custom, the larger village, Halvergate, was left to the elder son, Gilbert, and Wickhampton to William. Sir Valence's last breath was used on a wish for peace between the brothers.

At first things were peaceful enough, with each of the young men taking pleasure in his inheritance, riding around their land on fine horses and making plans for the future. They even met and shook hands in public, but the cynical villagers noted this with knowing nods, for they could see the storm clouds gathering. The next Spring, when the oxen were yoked ready for ploughing, the trouble started.

One field, just north of Wickhampton church, projected far into the boundary of Halvergate. Gilbert saw this and called to his brother, "That field should be mine. It is an obvious mistake, made when the boundaries were drawn."

"You have enough already," replied William in a steel-cool voice. "No mistake has been made."

Gilbert was annoyed that his brother did not give way to him, jumped out of his saddle, ran over to William and pulled him from his horse. "I will have my way," he shouted, and struck out at William. At this the brothers attacked each other with a ferocity that frightened the sturdy country folk who had gathered to watch the fight.

William and Gilbert, unarmed, tore at each other with bare hands, on the edge of the very field that they argued over. They pushed and kicked, thumped and pulled, grabbed and jabbed with unreasoning and inhuman fury. It was as if all of their differences, throughout their lives, were being fought out at that time. They became like vicious snarling animals: they savaged each other until flesh was torn and blood flowed. Throats and breasts were ripped open and, in a final burst of malice, the brothers gripped each other's hearts and tore them out.

Lifeless, they lay upon the ground, then the onlookers saw a divine figure appear on the earth where they lay. Some say it was an angel, come to atone for such an inhuman exhibition, but it turned both bodies into stone, then disappeared. In the stone fingers, each still clutched the heart of the other.

Silently, Gilbert and William were borne off to their respective churches and laid to rest but, in memory of their fury and their shame, the villages were renamed: Hell Fire Gate and Wicked Hampton. Over the years these names fell out of common usage and became Halvergate and Wickhampton as used today.

Just west of Wickhampton, at Southwood, a large iron ring forms the doorhandle of the disused church. Perhaps it is an old sanctuary ring as some say, but there is another possibility. At the bottom of waterlogged Callow Pit is supposed to be a chest of treasure, guarded by Old Nick. One moonlit night a couple of local men hooked up the chest, by its ringed handle, and had to struggle against a huge black hand which was pulling against them. The hand won, but the ring came away from the chest and was taken to the church to prove their story.

NIGHT RIDER OF THE GOG MAGOG HILLS

Although only three hundred feet high, the Gog Magog Hills are probably the highest point in the county of Cambridgeshire. From up there a person can revel in the fine views of the towers and spires of the university city. At the highest point is Wandlebury Camp, the site of many strange happenings.

Sir Osbert and his men clattered along the old Roman road, Via Devana, hurrying to reach the Gog Magog Hills where they planned to stop for the night.

These Norman soldiers wore coats of mail, metal helmets with a forepiece which extended downwards to cover their noses, and carried lances in their hands. The clanking of their armour drowned out the sound of the muffled hoof beats on the grassy sward. This strong martial appearance was not deceptive, for these men had just taken part in a battle.

This was the year of 1075 and the Earls of Norfolk and Hereford had taken advantage of William I's temporary absence in Normandy to try to take sovereignty of the country for themselves. The attempt was quelled by soldiers loyal to William as they fought at Beecham in Norfolk.

A band of twenty Norman soldiers was despatched to Hereford to deliver news of the failed insurrection and it was these men, led by Sir Osbert, who approached the Gog Magog Hills.

Sir Osbert wiped the perspiration from his face and held up his hand to halt his men. He could see a village just ahead of them and hoped that this would provide their base for the night. Casual hospitality was quite normal in those days and strangers could usually be sure of finding at least a bed of straw under a sound roof. In this case Sir Osbert and his men were welcomed by the village headman, who organised immediate liquid refreshment for the men and safe keeping for their horses. A message was sent to the Lord of the Manor, Gilbert Fitzherbert, that extra food was needed and preparation for an impromptu banquet began.

Later that evening, after a splendid meal had been enjoyed by everyone and the company had been mellowed by the flowing wine, the village Teller of Tales, Stephen Shiner, stood up to entertain them.

Stephen told the old tales of Gog and Magog, the last of an ancient race of giants who were buried nearby, of a great and enormous horse which had its last resting place near their village, and also of a golden chariot buried beneath Mutlow Hill. He recounted the story of Boudica and how she had refortified the Iron Age stronghold of Wandlebury Camp, on the summit of the hills, in her fierce resistance against the Romans.

All of these stories were exciting and well told but the best was yet to come, because it was more relevant to their way of life. Stephen spun the story of a mysterious night rider who ruled the camp and was invincible against any mortal in combat. Anyone brave enough to challenge the night rider had to ride into the camp in the moonlight and cry out, "Knight to knight, come forth!" The warrior would appear on a jet black horse and joyfully accept the challenge.

One of Osbert's men happened to look out of the window and noticed that it was a moonlit night. "Why not challenge the night rider, Sir Osbert?" laughed the soldier.

Always one to acept a dare - indeed, that was how he had attained his rank - Osbert, by now quite intoxicated, replied positively. Very soon he found himself being carried away by the company, dressed in his armour and on his way up the Hills to Wandlebury Camp.

"This is the place, good sir," said Stephen Shiner. Without fear (hardly believing the story anyway!), Osbert rode out alone, leaving his companions huddled under the trees where they had a good view of the centre of the camp.

The moonlight shimmered on the bushes and the old earthworks threw long black shadows across the clear patches of ground. Osbert's armour gleamed a ghostly silver in the moonlight and his lance flashed as he raised then lowered it into the jousting position.

"Knight to knight, come forth!" he shouted out in a clear strong voice. The wind sighed softly through the branches and a fox cried out eerily, but nothing else happened. Moments passed then Osbert repeated his cry. Again he waited.

Suddenly there was a rustling in the bushes and a knight appeared, as predicted, his face hidden by the shadow of his helmet, clad in shining armour, riding a great black horse and carrying a silver lance.

Osbert rode out to meet him, halted, and both knights raised their lances in salutation. Osbert felt no fear, only a curiosity and a nudge in the stomach, just as he usually felt before a tournament.

Both knights began their charge and, as they passed, their lances clipped. Turning at the end of the run, they charged once more and Osbert saw, with a deep feeling of horror, that the night rider's lance was untipped as if in battle, not tipped as for jousting. At once the residue glow of the wine left him and he shifted his lance slightly. As the two knights met, Osbert's hooded lance prodded the night rider in the upper chest and pushed him off his horse. There was a growling shout from the watchers, but Osbert found the silence of his fallen adversary unnerving. He reined in and walked his horse over to the knight lying still and quiet on the grass. The watchers, silent now, stood still too.

Osbert circled and looked at the beautiful black horse, now grazing quietly. Having vanquished the mystery rider, it was fair to take his horse as a prize so he gathered the reins and led it off quietly. As he passed the motionless figure, Osbert looked down but there was still no sign of life. Rather anxious to leave by now, he spurred his horse on to a trot, but at that moment the fallen knight lifted himself up and hurled his lance at Osbert, catching him in the thigh and piercing the skin.

Thoroughly alarmed now, the whole party hurriedly returned to the village, pleased not to be followed! After the horses were tethered, the men went back to their wine goblets, animatedly talking about the events of the evening which gave Stephen Shiner a new story to add to his repertoire.

Eventually all was quiet in the Great Hall as, one by one, the visitors fell asleep, some at the table and some in the straw on the floor.

The morning light brought two surprises: first, it was discovered that the black horse had disappeared. Men were sent up to Wandlebury Camp and came back to report the second surprise: there were no signs that anything had happened there the previous night, not even trampled grass. But there *was* the wound in Osbert's thigh which was still fresh and open.

Nobody ever rode out again to challenge the night rider but, on the anniversary of the challenge, the wound on Sir Osbert's thigh opened up and bled again, exactly as if it had been freshly afflicted.

TWO WITCHES FROM LOWESTOFT?

Now overshadowed by its near neighbour,
Great Yarmouth, Lowestoft was, in the 1600s,
one of the premier fishing seaports
of the southern North Sea.
Most Lowestoft men worked on the fishing boats,
then as now, and many women
were employed in cleaning, salting and smoking
the mackerel and herring. Other
women acted as childminders,
and this story is about two of those.

Dorothy Durent spent her days cleaning and salting the fish caught by her husband and their fishermen neighbours. Dorothy had a child, a little boy called Peter, and he was looked after by a Miss Amy Duny who also looked after nine other children.

On fine days the children would play in Amy's backyard but when it rained they stayed indoors on the kitchen floor. It was a large kitchen, but untidy, and there was usually a smell of not particularly good ingredients (such as bones and scraps of meat or fish) cooking over the stove. Not a pleasant aroma and the children did not look forward to going to Amy's house on wet days. She would say, when questioned, that looking after children did not pay her enough to eat well. Amy Duny was a large, raw-boned woman, with a gaunt face and grey hair swept back from a broad forehead. She was not attractive and her voice was strident. Sometimes the children happily went to her house, but not always, and on these occasions they would complain to their mothers about their minder. Other children in the neighbourhood were looked after by another helper, Rose Cullender, and experienced similar conditions, complaining to their mothers too.

One day, Peter Durent had a fit and lay, screaming and frothing at the lips, on the floor. When she came to collect him, Peter's mother was told that he was not a good boy at all and quite tried Amy's patience. Dorothy was displeased and, once more, talked to the mothers of other children in Amy's care. It seemed that Peter was not the only one to be affected by Amy: three were very quiet, one cried at night and four stuttered quite badly. A new childminder was found for their offspring, but the troubles did not end. Peter's fits became worse and his mother took him with her to consult Margaret Lound, a white witch. Could she cure him?

This woman questioned Mrs Durent about Amy and Peter, then instructed her to take her child home and wrap him in a blanket that had been hung up in a chimney, then to burn anything that fell out of it. She did as she was told and was shocked to see a big toad falling out of the blanket. Dorothy hastily grabbed it in her tongs and threw it onto the fire - and it exploded like gunpowder! Very excited, she ran round to confront Amy Duny. Imagine her reaction when she found Amy in a poor condition, her face, and what could be seen of the rest of her, appearing to have been severely scorched.

There could, of course, have been an explanation but the neighbours were told the story immediately and, as one body, they marched to the justices with complaints that resulted in the prosecution of Amy Duny *and* Rose Cullender, on charges of bewitching children and practising sorcery.

At the trial, the judge, Sir Matthew Hale, listened to their trumped up charges but found plenty of evidence for them! There were witches, he said, for the Scriptures said so, and insofar as there were laws against witchcraft, this was further evidence that witches existed! Three days after the trial, on March 13th, 1664, Amy and Rose, protesting their innocence, were hanged in the market place.

Even in those crazy days, this could not be called justice.

Further Injustice

In the 16th and 17th centuries, anyone even slightly weird was afraid of being called a witch, for the sentence was always 'death'. Matthew Hopkins was the most famous witch hunter in England and in 1645 he vowed to rid East Anglia of its witches. It is said that he was responsible for the demise of over 400 'witches'. One who suffered unjustly at the hands of this Witchfinder General was the Suffolk Vicar of Brandeston, 80 year old John Lowes.

Years of humble labour had he given to the people of his parish but, towards the end of his life, no-one had a kind word to say for him. They approved of the ideas of the Puritan Parliamentarians, despising the foppish, Popish ways of their squire. The squire was the patron of John Lowes, however, and John felt that it was his duty to speak up for him. He could not forget the old ideals of his youth when God, King and country were all important. So, his was the crime of loyalty to his patron and to his king and, with nothing else to hold against him, John Lowes was found guilty on a trumped up charge of witchcraft. This happened mainly because, over a number of days of continuous taunting and questioning, he signed a false statement admitting guilt.

John Lowes was hanged in March 1645, after saying the burial service over himself. Those were dark days, when some people could live easily with such things on their conscience.

CRAZY MARY

I was walking along the cliffs near Pakefield on a lovely summer day. The footpath dipped and rose as it followed the whispering grass of the sun-kissed, sea-breezed cliff tops, with the sparkling blue sea gently washing the golden sands beneath. The clear blue sky was as wide as only East Anglia knows, and it was good to be alive. Suddenly the air chilled.

Just beyond the remains of the towers of the old Pakefield Lighthouse, the path dipped low into a deep hollow and my feet followed it incautiously. Down at the bottom the sea lost its apparent warmth, the air seemed chilly and damp and the clammy grass lay still. With quicker steps I walked on and up, out of the hollow, and with great relief found that the air became warm again. I did not look backwards.

"Ah, that's Crazy Mary's Hole," crinkled the face of an ancient who I saw at the hostelry in Pakefield, and the story of the hollow crackled from his lips.

Mary, a servant maid, was one of the young beauties of Pakefield, and her sweet young face was as brown as a berry with large, dark, laughing eyes and ruby red lips, just made for kissing. Her back was straight and she carried herself smartly, smiling happily at the world. Her heart was light and freely lent but rarely given. It seemed that there was a bright future for Mary and she regarded tomorrow's prospect with a gay confidence. The sons of merchants eyed her keenly, many of them courting her for her favours, and so did young farmers and one young lawyer. All of them willing to gamble and lose, the slightest chance of winning being prize enough.

These were the days of sailing ships and the full-bown sails of craft from many lands could be seen ploughing through the blue-grey waters just off Pakefield on most days. Mary was fascinated by the romance of sea and sail and was often to be found on the cliffs gazing away as if calling to some far world.

Then came the day that Mary lost her heart and, some say, her mind. As she went shopping for her mistress she saw a bronzed, handsome fellow, with dark curly hair and the unmistakable garb and gait of a man of the sea. Shopping forgotten, Mary and the stranger were drawn together. None heard the words they spoke, but many saw their heads together and the gentle glances between them as they took the clifftop path. It was a lovely day, with sunshine and soft breezes, and the hours just slipped away.

Along the cliff top path she strayed,
Beside her sailor lover,
And looked into his eyes that made
A heaven of blue above her.
He kissed her lifted lips, and she
Of kissing was not chary.
"The day that I come back from sea
I here will meet my Mary."
"Each morn," she said, "for thy dear sail
I here will watch the billow,
Nor here at dark hour will I fail
Before I press the pillow."

They parted, he to go back to his ship and she to the house where she worked. But Mary kept her word, visiting the cliff tops daily, though always in vain. Her face became haggard with worry, her large eyes staring. Her suitors deserted her eventually as she spent even more time haunting the cliffs.

Months passed but not Mary's longing for her sailor. Longing became yearning and yearning became a needing that this world could not endure. Her love tore at her heart during those long hours of waiting and watching, and Mary lost all interest in living. It became impossible for Mary to keep her job, so she haunted the cliff top pathway through night and day until life became too difficult to bear. One gusty March day her thin demented body was found on the beach.

"I hope she found her sailor in the dawn of her new day," mused the ancient as he thumbed his foaming glass. "That was a long time ago now," he went on, "but for Mary's sake don't go near that old hollow at dusk. There are sights and sounds there not of this world." I did not and would not for, though his lips smiled, his eyes did not falter as he put his knarled hand upon a lawyer's leatherbound tome.

HEREWARD THE WAKE

Ely's famous Cathedral, rising from the plain of the Fens, is a landmark that can be seen for miles. It is a beautiful and peaceful place now but this was not the case in 1069. Ely was the scene of the last stand of Hereward the Wake as he led the final resistance to the man soon to be known as William the Conqueror.

News of the defeat by the Normans of King Harold at Hastings in 1066 eventually filtered through to the depths of the Fenlands.

At this time, Cambridgeshire was a part of the Earldom of Walthof, who had been won over to the Norman cause by promises of a marriage to a distant niece of King William. This did not gain the allegiance of the population, however, and resistance to the Normans developed around a true man of the Fens - Hereward the Wake. He knew the marshes and waterways so well that outsmarting him was difficult indeed. There are many legends about Hereward the Wake, not all of which are believable, but this account at least is true.

Hereward was a born marshman who held lands in the Fens, mainly grazing lands but also some higher tracts of land which were cultivated. He was a huge man, rough in his ways, but kind and gentle to both people and animals. He was fiercely protective of his own lands and villagers, however, and, whilst still young, he fought someone older and stronger over a young girl who was betrothed to one of his own men. They cast aside their staffs and swords and Hereward advanced upon his opponent with fists raised. Parrying the other's blows with difficulty, Hereward delivered a tremendous blow to the man's jaw and sent him flying to the ground. Neither was he afraid to fight with his great sword. Many were the times when he wielded this to great effect and it truly deserved the name that Hereward had given it: Brainbiter. Dearest amongst his possessions was a great black horse, called Swallow, with white flashes on his two back feet. It was handsome, could outrun any other horse, and was sure-footed, even on the narrowest path through the marshes.

Section of the Bayeux Tapestry showing the Norman knights charging

Hereward made it his business to kill any Norman who came anywhere near his lands. His example encouraged others to similarly use the difficulties of penetrating the marshes. Gradually the thegn and peasants looked to him for leadership against the Invaders and then his fame spread further abroad. Other powerful and influential men from further north joined him, bringing along their peasants. A particularly useful addition to the ever-increasing army was Bishop Egelwine of Ely Abbey who pledged his assistance, along with his monks.

They proved their worth not only by their prayers, which were frequently offered up for the preservation of Hereward and his followers, but also for the potential for disguise which their clothing afforded in the guerilla war in which they became involved.

At long last, in 1069, William of Normandy became determined to crush this last pocket of resistance and sent a force to the Fens. They found out where Hereward was camped out in the marshes and, rather foolishly, began to build a causeway with branches of willow and alder. By the time this was completed, Hereward, unbeknown to his opponents, had flown. When the Normans were crossing the causeway, it sank beneath the weight of the mail-coated men, causing the swamp to be filled with terrified soldiers who were slowly smothered by the black mud.

No doubt William swore many an oath when news of this tragedy filtered through to him and, straightaway, he sent another group of soldiers to find Hereward, who was then using Ely Abbey as a base. Tracking Hereward down could not have been easy, but they were successful and eventually set to building a stronger causeway across the marsh. But when these men were crossing, Hereward set the dry reeds they had used in its construction alight, so that a great fire swept over it, causing the death of many men. The causeway remained, however, and when the fire had burnt itself out the soldiers crossed the marshes and arrived at the gates of the Abbey. The monks were terrified and allowed the fierce looking Norman soldiers in, and thus fell both Hereward's stronghold and the resistance.

Legend has it that, when the Normans broke through, Hereward was away searching for food and as William was so impressed by him, no serious search for the resistance leader ever took place. An alternative source claims that Hereward the Wake died during the breakthrough, but it seems likely that he survived. There is still a family in Northamptonshire today with the name of Wake who proudly proclaim that they are descendants of the last unconquered Englishman. It also seems likely that Hereward eventually made his peace with his arch-enemy, William the Conqueror.

The Ely Riots

Over the centuries The Isle of Ely saw many changes, with the draining of the Fens probably affecting the people more than anything else. Over the years they became used to being surrounded by land perfect for agriculture, with work for all who needed it.

There was widespread unemployment after the Napoleonic War due to the enclosure of common lands. Many agricultural workers and their families went hungry, even though they had tried every legal means possible to improve their lot. Perhaps they thought that shock tactics may work, so they burned stacks of corn, and machinery, then marched to the local vicar, the Reverend J Vachell, and demanded bread and work. The men were turned away and, already highly excited and under the influence of alcohol, eventually felt that they had no choice but to riot, pillage and steal food. The yeomanry turned out and made seventy-six arrests, but a number of people were hurt and one rioter was killed.

At the Special Assizes many were sentenced to imprisonment, some were transported and five were sentenced to death.

William Beamiss, George Crow, John Dennis, Isaac Harley and Thomas South were taken to the gallows at Mill Pits, along St John's Road, and were executed on June 28th, 1816. Their bodies were buried together, in one grave, in St Mary's church yard, an exception to the rule which forbade the interment of criminals in sanctified ground. They died because they and their fellows were hungry, and wanted to work. A plaque on a buttress on the church wall reminds us of their awful fate.

THE HEART OF THE TUESDAY MARKET PLACE

Essex is best known as witch country but Norfolk has its fair share too. Probably the witch of Kings Lynn is the most famous because there is remaining evidence still. There are various accounts of the one story and this is an interpretation of one of them.

Margaret Read lived down one of the many small alleys that ran down to the busy quays on the River Ouse. Her small house had crooked windows and a rough door set in its plastered walls: enough to make a modern estate agent drool. The little diamond window panes were somewhat dusty and edged with cobwebs but this did not stop some passersby glancing into the dark interior. Nobody who knew the place well looked in, though, for in the last quarter of the 16th Century, Shady Meg, as Margaret was known, was a feared woman. The superstitious folk of those times looked upon her with dread and awe for they believed that she was a witch.

After her death, people felt able to talk about Meg safely and it was said that she inherited her black powers from her aunt, Agnes Shipwell, who had died in nearby Grimston at the early age of 27.

When Margaret Read first came to live in Kings Lynn she became the confidante of several hags of the poor streets and, as the years passed, she gained the reputation of being able to make strange things happen. She had a narrow, sharp face, a scrawny neck and whispy grey-brown hair: she looked like a witch and seemed to have powers unavailable to the ordinary folk. Soon a small trickle of people with troubles began to visit Shady Meg's house but nothing could make them tell what went on inside. Entry to the house was strictly limited and because people were unsure, gossip started about the little things that they saw. For instance, why had a large spider made his home unmolested in the corner of Meg's window? Why had a plague of mice ruined sacks of flour in Mr Homlit's shop on the corner? Why did Mr Scase's dog die so suddenly? How did she get the money to support herself? Was that evil smoke coming from her chimney at the strangest times and even in the middle of summer? These and other things made the Kings Lynn folk suspect Shady Meg and she was continually being watched and gossipped about.

One particular visitor caught the gossips attention: the young and pretty Marion Harvey, who had recently born a child. Common tongues wagged and the rumour gained ground that Nick Kirk was the father and he had just taken up with another woman. As Marion's face seemed pinched with vengeance when she visited Meg late in the evenings, the streets were alive with premonition. What evil was being cooked up in that cottage?

Nick Kirk laughed when he heard the rumours but his laughter was silenced a week later when he felt severe pains in his chest and stomach. Three days later he was dead, and his parents immediately suspected the occult powers of Margaret Read and reported her to the authorities.

The Guards came and bore her away, screaming and shouting, from her cottage, then searched it thoroughly. There was a vast, mysterious horde of clutter, amongst which was found a small figure of a young man with pins thrust through his chest and stomach.

According to the custom of the time, Margaret was tried by ducking. She was bound, hands and feet, a long line was affixed to her neck and she was thrown in to the River Ouse. She was seen to float for a while, then she went under the water, with fury on her face and curses coming from her mouth.

The sinking body dragged the line through the hands of those who held it and, after what seemed an age, Captain Gotts of the Guard gave the order to haul in. Shady Meg came up coughing and gasping but alive and thus it was assumed that, because she had not drowned, she must be a witch. The penalty for practising witchcraft was death by burning and so she was taken away and locked up until preparations could be made.

A whispering crowd gathered on the morning of July 20th, 1590, on the Tuesday Market Place. They watched as a pile of faggots was built up around a central stake, then Shady Meg was brought out and tied to it. The faggots were fired and a dull flame and swirling smoke hid the 'witch' from view. The mesmerised onlookers saw occasional glimpses of her wrestling with her bonds but, as the flames grew higher, she suddenly gave a loud shriek, then a bang was heard. A missile was seen to fly from the fire and the crowd gasped as they saw that Shady Meg's heart had flown from her body and had struck the wall!

A week later it was noticed that, on the identical spot where the heart had hit the wall, a spider had cast a web over a newly fitted brick: a brick that was diamond shaped and had a heart carved in it.

Was it Margaret Reed,
or was it Mary Smith?

The story of the heart on the wall of the King's Lynn market place comes in more than one version, thus clearly showing the difference between historical fact and a folktale or legend. Some 'historical facts' are extremely well documented, but not necessarily at the time, therefore allowing errors to creep into history.

In an alternative account of the Heart of the Tuesday Market Place story, the witch in question was a Mary Smith who was burnt in 1616. Some say it was her heart which became implanted on the wall. Whoever it did belong to, the brick is there for all to see in a building at the furthest point away from the town centre.

If you visit the Old Gaol House, through the Kings Lynn Tourist Information Centre in the Saturday Market Place, you will hear the story of another witch, Mary Taylor. She was charged, along with her friend, George Smith, and found guilty of murdering the landlady of the Queen's Arms in the High Street. George was hanged and Mary was burned at the stake, and in the Gaol visitors can learn of their story. Go into one small room and you will see a reconstruction of a burning at the stake; next door there is a gibbet. This visit can give great amusement, and an insight to past crime and punishment, to young and old alike and is highly recommended.

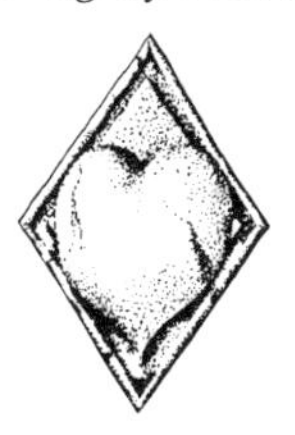

EAST BERGHOLT'S FAMOUS CONNECTIONS

In the winding lanes of southern Suffolk,
by the gentle waters of the River Stour, is the
small village of East Bergholt.
There are beautiful old houses,
broad rolling fields and tall thick hedgerows:
Constable country at its best.

Into this landscape was born the painter, John Constable, in 1776. His father owned several wind and water mills and travelled around the countryside in a pony and trap checking that the great stone wheels continued to grind. Young John often accompanied his father, and marvelled at the beauty of his surroundings. At a very early age John began drawing what he saw: the woods of oak, elm and ash, the sloping uplands of corn, the flat rich meadows where the cattle browsed in lazy herds, and the cottages and farmsteads where the simple people lived. He often spent hours away from his home in East Bergholt, capturing the landscape on his sketchpad. When he was seventeen, John Constable went to live in London, determined to learn to paint well, and learnt by copying the great masters over and over again.

The British did not appreciate his art then and Constable was unable to sell enough of his work at home. He exhibited his paintings in France and became immensely popular there. It was not until after his death that he was recognised in England as the great painter that he had become.

Now, that part of Suffolk bordering the River Stour, between Nayland and Manningtree, is known as Constable Country.

Another famous name connected to East Bergholt is that of

Thomas Wolsey, Chancellor of all England and Cardinal of the Church in the time of Henry VIII. Important he may have been, but not in East Bergholt: there his name was scoffed at. The villagers blamed him for their lack of a bell tower for their church!

Wolsey was born in Ipswich in 1471, a brilliant boy, son of a cattle dealer and butcher. At the age of eleven he entered Magdalen College at Cambridge, gaining a Bachelor of Arts degree four years later. For a while he was known as 'The Boy Bachelor'.

After his meteoric rise to power, Wolsey wanted to put something back into his home county and, amongst his grander projects, he began to build a fine college in Ipswich. He also began the building of a bell tower for East Bergholt church.

Cardinal Wolsey was not co-operative over the divorce of Henry and Catherine and, as a result, he was charged with high treason and was actually on his way to imprisonment in the Tower of London when he died. After the Cardinal's fall from power, Henry ordered that the college be torn down and, to the everlasting shame of East Bergholt, the church tower was never completed.

To this day, the bells are still housed in a timber bell-house in the churchyard.

DOGGED PERSISTENCE

Most of the ghostly dog stories from East Anglia concern the creature generally known as Black Shuck, but this one is different. The Shuck stories usually involve someone being led, or frightened, to their death. This dog seems to have been quite harmless if left alone, even lovable.

The pleasant Essex village of Hatfield Peveral, near Chelmsford, was haunted by the apparition of a big black dog for many years. He quietly padded from one gate of Crix House to the other, minding his own business, but still frightening small children and hapless tourists alike.

One day a local youth, driving his cart back from market, decided to stop and try to liven the old beast up, to try and rouse it to some sort of supernatural ire. His method was simple: he gave the creature a firm slap across its hindquarters with a riding crop! The ghost dog just turned and looked at him with a hurt expression on his face, much to the amusement of the carter and his audience. But they laughed too soon because at that moment a lightning bolt shot down from the sky and struck the tormentor, burning him to a crisp.

Afterwards the villagers wisely decided that it was best to leave the ghost dog to its own devices, and so he continued padding away until a fateful day early this century.

A new invention, the motor-car, had found its way onto the quiet lanes of rural Essex, and many villagers turned out to see the wonder. In the distance the roar of the engine was heard, growing louder as it neared, and everyone looked forward to their first glimpse of the machine. The ghost dog, however, clearly felt differently because he placed his tail firmly between his legs, lowered his front half and partially covered his eyes with his big shaggy paws. Soon the car hurtled into the village street and this was too much for the ghostly dog: his eyes widened in amazement, he let out a piteous wail and exploded into a mass of flames!

For once, modern technology seemed to get the better of something from the spirit world. Perhaps the sight of the car drove him over the edge, or perhaps he hides out in this sleepy village, occasionally partitioning his MP for a bypass, but he has not been seen from that day to this.

Strange Haunts, even for Ghosts

Until a few years ago an old railway carriage was kept at Cressing, in Suffolk, and now it it can be seen at Elsenham, in Essex. It is special, for it has an unusual history, and houses a ghost!

This was the last coach in Winston Churchill's funeral train, but the ghost is not that of the great statesman. It is the revenant of a girl murdered in the coach many years ago.

Although it is now disused, the carriage has been used as a restaurant in the past and there is always the possibility of it being a hive of human activity again.

At Bircham Newton in Norfolk, there is now a training centre for the building and construction business. It is built on the site of a World War One RAF base and some of the original buildings are still being used.

Fliers from both World Wars enjoyed the facilities of this camp, including the use of the squash courts. Many of them lost their lives in enemy skies, including one pilot who died in March, 1917. At midnight on a particular day in March, each year, he returns to keep his date on the squash courts. Many have seen and heard him, and few doubt his presence.

TOM HICKATHRIFT
Giant of the Fens

In the Norfolk Cambridgeshire border
area near Wisbech there are a
number of memorials to this legendary giant.
There is an effigy in Walpole St Peter's church
and old stone crosses in the vicarage gardens at both
Terrington St John and Tilney All Saints.
Hickathrift House, Farm and Corner are all
near Wisbech and there are
carvings on the Sun Inn at Saffron Walden relating to him.
We have to assume that the legends have substance.

A long time ago, back in the middle ages, in a Cambridgeshire village close to Wisbech, lived a farm labourer called William Hickathrift and his wife. They were a poor but happy and devoted couple and were quite content with their lot when the baby they had longed for was born.

The child, a boy they named Thomas, was a big bouncing baby who turned into a rather large toddler, growing so rapidly that by the time he was ten years old he was six feet tall.

Big, he certainly was, but Tom was not a clever chap. The lessons needed for life were not well learned and legend says that he was also exceedingly lazy. He did not help his parents in their daily endeavours, preferring to sit by the fire and watch it sparkling and crackling in the hearth. Even after his father died Tom's ways did not change, and his mother had to work hard to keep them in food and shelter.

It is said that a Wisbech farmer felt so sorry for Mrs Hickathrift that he offered her two bundles of straw - if she could find someone to take them home for her. After a lot of grumbling and nagging, Tom at last took himself off to the field where the straw lay, laid a long rope on the ground and tied in it as much straw as would normally be held in a wagon. The farmer looked on, horrified, as Tom took this first bundle home, carried so easily on his shoulder. Reluctant to back down on his offer, but hoping to weigh Tom down during his next trip, the farmer hid some large stones in the straw stack. But they made no difference to this giant of a boy. A few times on his trip home he heard something drop but thought that it was grain from carelessly threshed straw, not rocks dropping out of his bundle.

On another occasion, he was asked to help load a woodman's cart and was aggravated to see five men using hoists and pulleys. Ordering them aside, he loaded the wagon on his own, lifting whole tree trunks as though they were mere sticks. As a payment he took on his shoulders, and walked home with, a tree which was said to have been heavier than the whole load on the cart!

Following these feats of strength, Tom did not have a problem finding employment. He was given a job carting beer from King's Lynn to Wisbech. The journey between these two towns was made all the longer because Tom had to take a roundabout route to avoid the land of a fierce giant who had terrorised the Fenlanders for years.

One day, after Tom had eaten a huge lunch and had supped a deal of ale, he decided to use the direct route, across the giant's land. As he drove his wagon along, Tom was spotted, challenged and told to go back. The huge owner of the land pointed to a row of heads hanging from a rail and told Tom that that was what happened to people who intruded on his property. Inside Tom, though, the beer still boiled and he was bold enough to say, "I'm not afraid of you. Or of them either, come to that," pointing at the ghastly bodiless trophies.

The giant ran back to his house and soon returned brandishing a large club. Tom was totally unarmed but thought quickly for once. He jumped down from the wagon, tipped it over and snatched off a wheel to use as a shield and an axle to use as a club. The two giants were quite evenly matched, both were furious, and so the fight was long and hard. Neither asked for or gave mercy but, slowly, Tom's youth began to count for him. His opponent was unused to being challenged by equals, and out of condition, so eventually he was on the ground and at Tom's mercy. There was no compassion - and his head was separated from his shoulders.

Tom went on to the other giant's house and there found riches beyond his dreams. There was enough gold and silver to keep him and his mother for the rest of their lives, and they never needed to work again.

It is said that Tom Hickathrift is buried in the churchyard at Tilney All Saints but, as with many legends from the distant past, there is no remaining proof.

Let's Be Sizist!

There is no record now of the height Tom Hickathrift grew to, but another Cambridgeshire man was certainly said to be the tallest person in Britain at one time. James Toller was born in 1795 in St Neots and legend tells us that he was 8 feet 6 inches, or 259cm, tall. The truth of the matter was, though, that he was a foot less than this, making him three inches shorter than the tallest man in the country at that time. Unfortunately there are no real records kept of these things from before this century and truth becomes obscured by exaggeration.

Three feet smaller than James Toller, and once the lightest person in Britain, Robert Thorn was born in March, Cambridgeshire in 1842. At the age of 32 he weighed only 49 pounds, or 22kg, and this case is well documented.

THROUGH THE STREETS OF CAMBRIDGE

One of the truly beautiful cities in Britain, Cambridge has lost none of its medieval charm though there has been a recent burst of industrialisation. Its streets are a nightmare for motorists but a delight for the unhurried pedestrian, offering glimpses of hallowed lawns and colleges. Stories and spooks abound, so here are just a few.

It is temptimg to explore the beauties of the impressive walls and gateways, the charming bridges over the rippling river, the velvet lawns and the watchful weeping willows. To walk, to sit, to wander or to rest and watch - all are delightul, in the right weather, for both strangers and those who already know the city well. The gates invite us into the quadrangles of the universities which, in turn, invite us to look into the world of some of the many intriguing personalities.

Off Trinity Street stands Gonville and Caius College, which was founded by two Norfolk men. Edward Gonville, a rector, started the project and he died just two years after its completion in 1349. It was refounded in 1529 by John Caius, a Norwich physician, who rebuilt and extended his old college buildings after he had achieved fame and fortune. He ordered the building of three gates within the university; the gate of humility, the gate of virtue and the gate of honour. These, and indeed the whole design of the college, was supposed to represent the path a diligent student would have to follow. The second gate stands at the entrance to Caius' Court - a building that excites our interest for its stones have a special story to tell.

Caius College, Gate of Virtue

In 1539 a statute was passed which conferred upon Henry VIII all the property of the dissolved religious houses. Philip Paris, a Cambridgeshire magistrate, was instructed to take all the treasures of the Fenland abbeys and dispose of the lands and buildings. Richard Cromwell bought the abbey sites, and the lands that went with them, for £4,663.4s.2d and then set about dismantling some of the buildings. Stones from Ramsey Abbey church were bought by John Caius and used to build Caius' Court. Imprisoned within its walls are the echoes of quiet-spirited mediaeval monks singing their chants - thought provoking indeed.

Just down the road is St John's College and its magnificent gateway is decorated with heraldic carvings, on the grounds of which are scattered daisies. Daisies are the emblem of the founder of the college, Lady Margaret Beaufort of Collyweston, near Stamford, who was the grandmother of Henry VIII. The heraldic antelopes bearing the arms of France and England are also those of the Beaufort family. Amongst the studies and rooms of St John's College is Staircase O, where a spectre has often been seen: the ghost of Dr Wood, a master of St John's who died in 1839. This ghost is not that of a grand figure clothed in the dignified robes of office, however, but that of a shivering humble student. Dr Wood reached his exalted position through scholastic endeavour but first was a poor student who could not afford the basic comforts of life. He wrapped straw around his feet to keep them warm and read by the flickering length of the guttering rush candle which badly illuminated the stairway. No wonder, then, that on gloomy winter evenings his spirit still lingers on the stairs; a creature of the shadows that cannot rest in peace.

Dr Butts was a very proud man who had every justification for being so. He was appointed Master of Corpus Christi College in 1626, thus fulfilling his primary ambition. Ever since his student days he had dreamed of being a Master, venerated by his students, within the confines of a Cambridge College. Corpus Christi was a college of noble traditions, having been founded in 1352 by the Guild of Corpus Christi and the Guild of the Blessed Virgin Mary. Dr Butts gloried in his position there, enjoying the opportunities to study and to teach his beloved students.

His joy did not survive, though, and as the winter of 1632 warmed into Spring, Dr Butts became increasingly depressed. The plague was rife in this overcrowded city, and many unfortunate students were contaminated and died. Others fled in time, to return to their homes, leaving the halls and rooms of the colleges still and silent. Dr Butts walked through the deserted rooms and echoing streets alone and the distress of the plague seemed unending to him. On Easter Sunday of that year the Master hanged himself in his room.

Students still speak of a chill, sinister presence in this place, not entirely attributable to the august present holder of the post of Master.

Nearly 50 years later, all the faces at Corpus Christi had changed and the Master of the College in 1676 shall remain nameless here. He was a stern man with a great daunting beard and an overwhelming presence. Just the right person for the job, in fact, as the students of the day were a very lively lot who often needed firm discipline. The good Master had a daughter.

Mirabelle was a black-eyed, black-haired beauty who inflamed the imagination of many a young man. The Master had to keep a very close eye on her, and on the students who came near her. He was once so proud of his sweet young child, but since blossoming into womanhood she had become a millstone around his neck. Mirabelle drew the students to her as moths to a flame, effortlessly, and delighted in their adulation.

There were many near escapes, for all knew what would happen if the Master caught anyone with his daughter. Early one evening, John Martin was courting the lovely Mirabelle in the kitchen below the Master's room when recognised steps were heard coming along the flagged corridor. Quickly, John dived into the cupboard and Mirabelle fastened the door behind him before sitting down to sew. The Master entered and sternly ordered the girl off to bed, for he wanted solitude after a difficult day. Mirabelle resolved to return when all was clear but the Master, warm before the kitchen fire, sat reading for hours.

He read on silently, and John Martin passed on silently too. It was a quarter to midnight before Mirabelle was able to return to the kitchen and open the cupboard door. She fainted right away as the inert body of the student tumbled out. Afraid to give himself away, he had suffocated in the stifling cupboard.

So John Martin's restless spirit haunts the college too: the life having been thrown away so carelessly, the soul is eternally searching for the destiny that should have been his.

Hobson's Choice

If the streets of Cambridge could tell their stories, one of the best would be from Hobson Street, just to the north side of Christ's College.

Over 400 years ago, Thomas Hobson inherited from his father a cart and eight horses - a carrier's business. He carted goods between London and Cambridge and also hired out horses to the men of the city.

Mr Hobson looked after his horses extremely well, never ill-treating or overworking them. To make certain that they had a proper amount of rest, he would only allow them to be hired in strict rotation. Customers were not allowed to choose the horse they wanted because of its looks, colour or reputation - instead they had to have the next one available. Because he was so consistent and fair, the phrase "Hobson's Choice", meaning no choice at all, became known throughout the country, and even beyond.

Thomas Hobson became quite wealthy because he was so reliable and thorough. He was generous too, and donated land to the city on which to build a workhouse for the poor. He lived for 86 years but died after his business had to close down because of the plague and fear of it spreading. His name lives on, though, for the stream which feeds the Market Hill fountain is known as Hobson's Conduit.

REBECCA OF LONG MELFORD

Long Melford Church is a very fine building,
paid for from the profits of the wool trade.
It is linked to the Rebecca of our
story because of one
of her exploits, but a number of strange things
happened to this Suffolk girl.

One October evening at the end of the 19th Century, a cheery scene was taking place in a plastered and thatched farmhouse at the southern end of Long Melford. The farm was owned by Walter Scase and he was enjoying the company of three friends, John Postle, Henry Sale and William Moss. The four farmers sat in the parlour, clad in their woollen tweed suits and great brown boots, quaffing great mugs of the mild Suffolk ale. Walter's wife had died of consumption four years earlier and he was looked after by a pleasant housekeeper and a young maid called Rebecca.

It was Rebecca who served the farmers this evening, taking away their empty mugs and returning them frothing to the brim, her lively personality pleasing the men. At about 10pm she came in with the mugs only half filled, and explained that the barrel in the kitchen was empty. It seemed that their evening's drinking must come to an end but Walter said that he would send Rebecca to the Greyhound Inn to fetch another gallon.

"But she'll be afeared," said Henry. "You know she'll hatta cross the churchyard."

Walter grinned and said that Rebecca would not be frightened to go. The others disagreed and a wager was made. Rebecca did not turn a hair at the request and came back later, not at all affected by her walk and carrying the pitcher of ale. Walter received the £5 wager, more ale was drunk and eventually the four retired.

The following week the farmers were once more sitting in that parlour and the talk came round to the apparent dauntlessness of the girl, Rebecca. Walter insisted that she was fearless and Henry, keen to get his money back, suggested that they set her a task.

"Would she go to the crypt of the church and get a skull?" Henry wondered. Walter thought so and another £5 wager was laid. When Rebecca was called in and the strange request put to her, she seemed unbothered and prepared to leave.

Pulling her shawl around her, the maid crossed the churchyard, lit her candle when she entered the church and headed for the crypt entrance. She saw something in white coming towards her, but, unfazed, Rebecca entered.

Once inside she picked up the first skull that she saw but put it down quickly when a sepulchral voice said, "Don't take that: that is my father." She moved along and picked up another but again the voice intoned, "Don't take that: that is my mother." Respectfully, Rebecca passed on to the third, but as soon as she touched that skull the voice echoed around the cold crypt, "Don't take that: that is my brother." Without waiting for the voice, she grabbed the fourth skull and ran out, back through the church, amidst much disembodied screeching and shouting.

Back inside the cosy farmhouse parlour, the four farmers chilled as she told her story. They rushed out, heading for the church, and soon found the verger, stone dead, with a sheet around him, at the door of the crypt.

This story quickly circulated around the village and was heard by the squire who had reasons of his own to ask Rebecca to go and work for him. She accepted and one of her jobs was waiting at the table where she always had to lay an extra place ..... for the ghost of the squire's mother. He had been haunted by this ghost for some time and it often took food from diners' lips at mealtimes. Rebecca had some knowledge of the supernatural, as did most people in those days, and successfully tried

to lay the ghost by crossing its knife and fork, much to the relief of her new employer.

Rebecca slept in a little attic room and, one night, a black fog appeared around her bed. It bewitched her and charmed her down to the cellar. There she saw two bags of gold, one large and one small, and a figure that told her the large one was for the squire and the other for herself.

Next day she told the squire about her 'dream' but said that the small bag of gold was for him. He collected the treasure from the cellar and, not doubting her but unable to control his lust for riches, later asked Rebecca to marry him, thus making her gold his.

Rebecca was very happy to become the wife of the squire, and rich too! She did not live happily ever after, though, because the squire, wealth having gone to his head, started drinking and wife-beating.

Which all goes to show that honesty is the best policy, even when dealing with the supernatural!

Spectres of Long Melford

Britain has more reported ghosts per square mile than any other country in the world and Suffolk is an extremely spooky county. The most haunted site in the country was at Borley Rectory near Long Melford in Suffolk, with a large amount of sightings being reported. The spectral activity there between 1863 and 1939 (when it was destroyed by fire) was truly phenomenal.

The Bull Hotel in Long Melford was built about 600 years ago as a wool merchants house. For four hundred years it has been an Inn and for 300 of those years it has been haunted by a murdered farmer, Richard Evered. It is said that ghosts do not live for ever and certainly the current management of The Bull say that nothing paranormal has been seen since the 1970s.

By the church is Kentwell Hall, built in 1578 and used today for Elizabethan costume events. The White Lady who haunts the Hall may be Countess Rivers, who supposedly threw herself into the moat, preferring death to one of her husband's parties!

BOUDICA
THE WARRIOR QUEEN OF EAST ANGLIA

Resistance to conquering invaders has always attracted admiration and Boudica's exploits throughout East Anglia were the talk of the age and the stuff of history. This Queen led some of the major offensives of the Ancient Britons against the Romans and deserves her name to be revered as one of the important daughters of Norfolk.

Boudica was born into the Iceni tribe whose main settlement was probably at Caistor St Edmunds, just south of present day Norwich. Many of the tribes in Britain at that time were war-like and the Iceni was certainly no exception. In 43AD, when Boudica was a teenager, the Iceni were preparing to do battle with the Catuvellauni tribe from Essex. This was a fight which did not happen, however, but only because the Romans conquered the Catuvellauni. Iceni elation was shortlived because just a few years later the Iceni lands were invaded and the Romans ruled their lives too. Indeed, it is thanks to the Roman chroniclers that anything of Boudicas's story remains.

Boudica married Prasutagus, the Iceni king, but he turned out to be nothing but a puppet of the Romans. Soon his bride was wishing for the overthrow of both her husband and his masters. Time went by and Boudica had two children, both girls, who were brought up in the warrier tradition of the Iceni tribesmen.

When Prasutagus died in 60AD he willed that a half of his kingdom should go to his daughters and the other half should be given to the Roman Emperor Nero. Not good enough for the Romans: they took everything, raped the women and gave Boudica a public lashing for fighting against them. She was incensed and immediately began to plan a revolt.

By this time Boudica was nearly 40 years old and, according to Roman historians, her hair was very long and white. She was every inch a queen, possessed a remarkable gift of oratory and was just what the Britains had been needing. It was not just her own Iceni warriors that flocked to her encampment: soon a force of several thousands had amassed and pledged their allegiance to her. They had long hated the cruel rule of the Romans and gladly began the march towards the Roman bases in the south of the country. Omens preceded their advance and it was reported that the Channel was said to have flowed red, houses were seen in the Thames and, in Colchester, the Roman statue to the the god Victory fell flat on its face.

Boudica and her revolutionaries enjoyed easy victories at Colchester, London and St Albans and they acted without mercy, killing thousands of Romans as well as Britons who had worked for the enemy. Recruits flocked to join the avengers, anxious to help beat the Romans, and knowing that there was a great battle ahead.

So far the opposition had not been massive. This was because the main Roman force had been over in Anglesey, carrying out the final round up and slaughter of the Druids. Suetonius Paulus, the Roman leader, was aware of what had been happening, however, and marched his men south/eastwards again when the Druids had been wiped out. The Roman forces were marshalled just to the north of St Albans and formed into the shape of a wedge; infantry in the centre and the cavalry on the wings. This was a familiar formation to them and one which they knew must be kept firm.

Disciplined and brave they undoubtedly were, but the Romans must have been concerned when they first saw the hordes of Boudica. Thousands of savage and ferocious tribesmen, so far jubilant and very confident of victory, rushed towards them, hurling their weapons and shouting abuse, with the women and children behind them yelling encouragement.

The Roman army stayed calm, maintained their wedge, and moved slowly but relentlessly forward, slaying all in its path and massacring thousands of Britons, including women and children.

Those who remained alive after Boudica's rebellion fled from the seemingly invincible slaughter machine to lick their wounds before heading for home. Boudica and her daughters all escaped but, knowing that they would be captured and killed, the Iceni Queen poisoned her daughters and then committed suicide by drinking poison. According to legend, her body was brought back to Norfolk by faithful followers and buried at Quidenham under a long low mound, about a quarter of a mile from the church.

The Romans wreaked a terrible revenge on the people of Norfolk for the savagery of Boudica at Colchester, London and St Albans and it took generations for the people of the area to recover and, by then, the Iceni Tribe no longer existed.

Reconstructions of our Past

Each of the East Anglian counties has within its borders an example of how people lived in Britain in ancient times.

In Norfolk there is the Cockley Cley Iceni Village, near Swaffham, which offers a wonderful opportunity to see how the Iceni tribe of Boudica lived. Here is a complete village, as it would have been nearly 2000 years ago, plus a Saxon church with a Roman coffin inside it.

Flag Fen in Peterborough answers archaeologist's prayers. There have been settlements here since the Stone Age and the Fenland Archaeological Trust has built reconstructions of ancient roundhouses and a visitor centre. More importantly, serious work goes on here and there is a wonderful indoor 'dig' to visit. Many finds are on display from the Bronze Age and a Roman road can be viewed too.

At West Stow, near Bury St Edmunds, there is a magical place: a replica of part of an Anglo Saxon village that existed there between the 5th and 7th centuries. There is a living history project going on here, all in a beautiful country setting.

After the Norman invasion in 1066, a number of wooden motte and bailey castles were built, including one on a hill in Mountfitchet in Essex, not far from Stansted airport. This reconstruction shows in great, and sometimes gory, detail how life was in a Norman stronghold, complete with authentic sounds and smells, including those of the livestock wandering around the compound.

JACK O'LANTERN

If there is a centre to the Fenland it would
perhaps lie in the area west of March,
north of Chatteris, east of
Whittlesey and south of Thorney.
Wide and bleak are the drained peatlands now,
but certainly, because of their
history, they are the keepers of secrets.

The broad, fertile, black Fenland fields stretch out to and beyond the horizon, with a stark ascetic beauty. Well scattered, houses and occasional treees dot the landscape, which is interlaced by drainage dykes and metalled roads. In the wide hours of sunlight Fenland seems at one with mankind, but in the gloomy and dark hours its face takes on another character. As clouds and night overwhelm the wide-skied flatlands, it is quite easy to imagine a time long past.

Ages ago there were wide stretches of wind-rippled water and scudding clouded sky, reed quivering channels, willow-lined pathways and, always in the distance, the grey stone of an abbey. Travellers who did not know their way looked for the paths, and tried to follow them, but some were inevitably lost in the bottomless mud. For the paths wound in and out of the clumps of reed, through and around the thickets of alders and willows, keeping to the firm ground which was was practically indistinguishable from the swamp. The thick black mud was hungry and tenacious, holding fast on to any who chanced to step off the path, before slowly, so slowly, sucking them down. You can imagine that its victims' arms and legs would search desperately for something to hold on to, but in vain and the awful ending was always the same. Afterwards there would be no sign that anyone had passed that way - only the last slurp of an air bubble from the mud in the grass.

Many years ago, as the early evening sun was setting on a day in late August, a local man strode through the Fenlands towards Thorney Abbey. He walked confidently along the well-trodden paths in the fading light, towards the grey towered mass in the far distance. He listened to the wind whispering through the reeds and to the bitterns, curlews and warblers as they passed on their goodnight messages. Over these sounds he heard his own footsteps, crunching through the dry grass of late summer.

The summer colours slowly but surely turned grey in the twilight as the man strode onwards along the winding, twisting footpath. The footpath too turned grey, and the shapes around him lost their definition. The man's stride faltered, his feet hesitated and then he stood still. His breath grew misty in the chilling air and wisps of mist wafted from the undergrowth. No longer could he hear the birds or the breeze - silence had descended over the Fenlands. The man's confidence evaporated for he could no longer make out the shape of Thorney Abbey, and he realised that he was lost in the treacherous swamp. His eyes could hardly see the pathway now and he had no hope of assistance.

All of a sudden, he saw a glimmering glow ahead and hurried towards it, thinking wrongly that it was a sign of a fellow traveller. Then another soft small glow lit up the immediate space in front of him and led his steps on. It was a Will-o-the-Wisp, or Jack o'Lantern, that creature of legend and dream, a mystery that no-one then understood. If he could have caught it, he would have seen a curious beetle, wingless, soft-bodied and grub-like. It was the female beetle, who clings to the grasses or sedges, and lights up to attract her mate, a small, narrow, grey-brown insect. She has control over her light, turning it off and on, or dimming it, as the occasion demands.

The man lost in the fens neither knew nor understood but he

certainly saw the softly glowing lights that glimmered on and off before him. He did *not* know the story that tells of these same lights leading unwitting walkers into the deepest swamps and certain death.

Firm ground beneath his feet encouraged him on and his confidence grew. Like fairies swinging their lamps before him, they made the man feel secure, as each step took him safely on through the darkness of the wild swamp. His imagination ran wild, seeing the fairy lantern bearers lighting his way past dead folk rising out of muddy pools, staring at him with fixed eyes, whilst slimy dead hands beckoned to him and clutched at the air behind his confident boots. Or was it imagination? Stepping lightly from tuft to tuft, he felt that if his foot slipped, hands of mud would hold him tight and hands of death would drag him down into slimy eternity. No-one would ever know what had become of him.

The creatures of the twilight continued to glimmer and glow, guiding his feet along pathways that eventually turned into a wide firm track that led out of the swamp and into Thorney.

With great relief, the man sat infront of a roaring fire that night, holding a mug of ale firmly in his hands, and told his friends about his awesome journey.

Later, he told the complete story to the monks from Thorney Abbey and one of them wrote it down. It is because of that monk that we know the story today: the famous tale of the Man of the Fens who was led by the Jack 0'Lanterns, the creatures who guide the good to safety. What happens to the bad? Well, they are lead astray.

Bells in the Mist

Pictured above is the 18th century Bull Hotel, and the taller Mansion House, as they were at the end of the last century. The Mansion House was built in the early 1700s and its first recorded owner was the Peterborough Member of Parliament, Matthew Wyldbore.

There is a well-known story about Mr Wyldbore which ensured that each year, at least once, he would be remembered.

One evening, Mr Wyldbore was returning to his home, across the fenlands, when the previously clear sky began to get misty, turning quickly into thick fog. Mr Wyldbore was in almost as much danger then as travellers a century earlier, before the marshes were drained. He was completely lost and it was not until he heard the familiar bells of St John the Baptist's church in Peterborough that he knew which way to turn.

Those bells guided him safely home that night and he was so grateful that he left provision for the bells to be rung every year on that day, and the custom survives still.

The Mansion House no longer exists. It was home to a great many doctors over the years but, as the city grew, its garden was needed for expansion of the street system. The decision to demolish it was taken in 1925.

THE TUDOR QUEENS IN EAST ANGLIA

The most obvious Tudor connection with this region is Anne Boleyn and Blickling in Norfolk, but it is by no means the only one.

Mary Tudor was born in 1495, the third daughter of Henry VII and the dowager queen of France. By a contemporary account she was "divinely pretty, soft, pleasant, gentle and charming", and another admirer wrote that "nature never formed anything more beautiful". Mary had most decisions about her life made for her and, at nineteen, was married by proxy to Prince Charles of Castile. This first marriage was annulled as the couple never met and she was married again that year, this time to King Louis XII of France. Mary went to Paris with a large dowry and received many marvellous wedding gifts, including the famed Mirror of Naples. This was a large diamond with a pearl hanging from it, suppposedly worth sixty-thousand crowns. Mary had been married less than three months when her husband died but she was not allowed to return to England until it was certain that she was not carrying a future King of France. During these weeks Mary dressed completely in white and, therefore, became known as La Reine Blanche, or the White Queen.

As she was not bearing a baby, her brother, Henry VIII, sent Charles Brandon, the Duke of Suffolk, to France to bring Mary, her dowry and all her possessions, home. Brandon and the Dowager Queen became attached to each other and returned to England as a married couple, much to the annoyance of the King. Placated by receipt of the dowry, the Mirror of Naples and other treasures, Henry agreed to a re-marriage at

Greenwich before the couple went to Brandon's home in Suffolk, Westhorpe Hall.

They had two children, a daughter Frances, and a son who died whilst still very young. Mary was very happy in Suffolk and wrote lovingly of the countryside and the picnics she enjoyed so much, but she died at Westhorpe in June 1533 when she was only 38 years old. She was buried in Bury St Edmunds and her body was moved after the dissolution of the monasteries to St Mary's Church where it still lies.

The last pages of the sad story of Catherine of Aragon were played out in the grand setting of Peterborough Cathedral. Her body now lies in the north aisle but once there was a grand black marble tomb marking the spot. It is said that this was demolished after 1764 and the materials used to ornament the Dean's summer house.

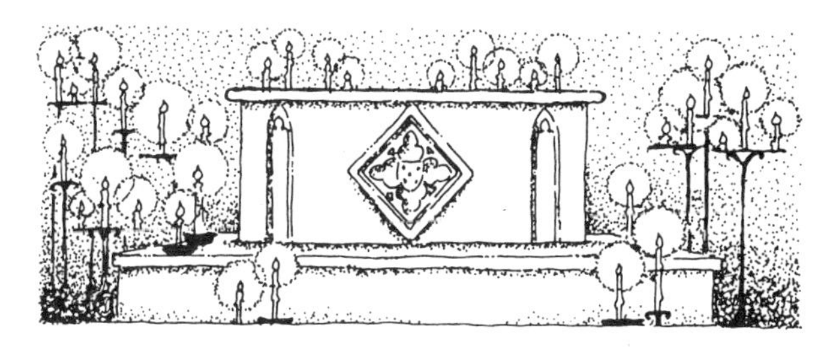

After Herny VIII divorced Catherine of Aragon in order to marry Anne Boleyn, she was cast out from the Court and lived the last years of her life at Kimbolton Castle, brokenhearted.

On 7th January, 1536 Catherine died and 20 days later a large wagon, drawn by six horses and attended by fifty hooded guards, carried her body over Kimbolton's drawbridge. The cortege spent the night at Sawtry Abbey before travelling on to Peterborough the next day. This funeral was the focus of the last great Catholic gatherings, but Henry VIII, meanwhile, celebrated the death of his first queen with a ball at Greenwich.

Filtering through the pages of history come tales of miracles taking place at the site of the tomb, along with an assertion that Peterborough Cathedral, alone in this part of Britain, was not ravaged in the Reformation due to the fact that Catherine was buried there.

It is possible that somewhere in Rainthorpe Hall in Nofolk lies the answer to a mystery that has remained unsolved for over 400 years. It is in the grounds of this Hall that two spirits meet and whisper together on the evening of September 8th each year.

By the time she was 17 years old, the beautiful girl born as Amy Robsart was already a widow. Her family was intertwined with that of her husband, Roger Appleyard, who was lord of the manors of Bracon Ash, Rainthorpe and Stanfield. Amy was extremely friendly with her half-brother, John Appleyard and they lived together at Stanfield Manor, with her family, for some time.

During the middle of the 16th Century there was a local uprising, which became known as the Peasants' Revolt, and soldiers came up from London to quell it. The leader of the soldiers was the Earl of Dudley who set up his headquarters close to Stanfield Hall. Amy's family sometimes entertained the Earl and his family and soon Amy fell in love with his son, Robert. They were married in London and the wedding was attended by the nobility of the land, including the young king, Edward VI.

Amy and Robert Dudley lived a rich and romantic life, visiting the various houses on the extensive Dudley estates all over the country. Their fortunes changed, however, when the king died and Robert's father was involved in a plot which ended in him being beheaded, the Dudley possessions being confiscated and Robert being imprisoned for a while in the Tower of London. After his release, the couple returned to Amy's

Stanfield home and spent happy years managing the lands thereabouts. Amy's half-brother and great friend, John Appleyard, lived at nearby Rainthorpe Hall and his presence aded greatly to Amy's happiness. Robert Dudley, known as the Earl of Leicester, was not so content and sought favour at the Court of Elizabeth I. The 'Virgin Queen' returned the confiscated land to the Dudley family and spent so much time with the Earl of Leicester that tongues wagged with tales of 'the king to be'.

Amy, back in Norfolk, was bereft when these stories reached her and her health suffered greatly. Deserted by her husband, Amy's weight plummeted, her face grew sallow and John Appleyard, amongst others, wondered whether she had a tumour, or was she being poisoned?

Whilst Amy was visiting Cumnor Hall in Berkshire, she died after falling down the stairs and when the news reached Rainthorpe Hall, John Appleyard openly swore that it must have been murder. He asserted that as Dudley and the Queen both benefited from Amy's demise they must have been involved in some sort of a plot to kill her. John was thrown in prison for his outspoken behaviour and not released until he apologised and agreed with the jury's verdict of accidental death.

It is the spirits of Amy Dudley and John Appleyard whispering outside Rainthorpe Hall each September; an eavesdropper may be able to discover whether Elizabeth I had a hand in Amy's tragic death.

Edmund - Saint and King of East Anglia

Memorials abound in Norfolk to Edmund, son of the King of Saxony. He was adopted by King Offa of East Anglia and left to take over this kingdom, hardly knowing his new father.

When Edmund was brought to England, he landed at Hunstanton where twelve springs gushed forth to mark the occasion. A chapel was built on the spot and remains of it are near the lighthouse. After some training in kingship, Edmund was crowned at Bury St Edmunds on Christmas Day, 855.

East Anglia was soon embroiled in battles with the invading Danes and Edmund proved to be a good and successful leader. The invaders were repelled and the East Anglians had ten years of peace before vengeance was wreaked.

There was a terrible battle near Thetford, leaving fields red with blood and the Danes victorious. Edmund escaped, but was pursued relentlessly. He was beseiged in a castle, chased over land and eventually found, betrayed, hiding under a bridge over a stream at Hoxne. Legend, even now, decrees that no bridal couple shall pass over this bridge.

Edmund was tied to a nearby oak tree and the Danes, who wanted him to renounce his Christianity, shot arrows at him. Edmund refused and so was decapitated. Grisly stories were told about the head shouting out to be re-united with the body, and miracles occurred at the shrine built on the site. It was even said that the body did not decay and that someone had the job of cutting the hair and nails of the corpse!

THE POTTER HEIGHAM DRUMMER

Potter Heigham today seems to be a place devoted to pleasure boating, but this has not aways been the case. At the beginning of the 1800s, it was particularly known for its rich farmland, and from then onwards it has been known for something else as well: its spectral visitor.

Potter Heigham was once a small village of rich farms, for on those flatlands of dark brown soil, crops grew richly and animals thrived on the lush pastures down by the river. Even where the meadow could not be drained and became marsh, men could still wrest a living from the bushes and vegetation which grew in abundance there. The young branches of the willow and alder were cut and stripped for weaving into baskets and the reeds and rushes, which could be mown, provided the finest thatching material in the country. Animals, birds and fish, fine for the dinner plate, could be trapped and caught, and living was good, if lean and cold in wintertime. The men who worked these marshes, living on their borders, were a mild, quiet breed, softly spoken and gentle, but could also be as tough and resisting as the lands and material of their trade.

Such a man was Jesse Ducker, who lived in Potter Heigham in 1814: a marshman and one of the best. He had a wife, Mary, and five children - two sons and three daughters. Jesse looked forward to fine jobs on the marshes for his sons and good marriages for his daughters. All of the children had different personalities but the eldest child, 18 year old Lilian, was the apple of her father's eye. She had soft brown hair, happy eyes and a roundness of face and figure that lent her a loveliness that made old men remember the dreams of their youth.

One cold February day Lilian was out in the village, running an errand, and well wrapped up against the weather, wearing a shawl over her head and a warm cloak around her. Even these heavy clothes could not hide her charms: charms that were noticed by a young soldier, home on leave. This was John Sadler of Hickling, resplendent in his uniform, whom Lilian had last seen five years ago when they often played on the marshes together.

Their eyes met, and so did their hearts, which beat with a warm passion that only young lovers know. They stood in the street and talked through the years that they had been apart, oblivious to the weather, and then Lilian invited John to come home with her. They sat in front of the fire in the cottage, planning for the future, for they had already decided that they wanted to be together.

When dusk whispered over the marshes in the late afternoon, Jesse came home and immediately saw his daughter's fascination with the soldier. He grew uncharacteristically harsh, saying that his Lilian was never going to marry a soldier. John protested that once the great battle was over in which he was to fight that summer, some said it was to be at Waterloo, he would leave the army and settle down.

"Let it be until then, John, " said Jesse, "but for now you will go." John left, but not before whispering to Lilian to wait at Swim Coots, a spot close to the edge of Hickling Broad on the Potter Heigham side.

The next evening at 4 o'clock, Lilian waited by the frozen Broad and was thrilled to the shivering marrow of her bones to hear first the roll of the drum, and then the swish of skates, as her soldier dramatically came to meet her. They talked and planned and whispered their love for each other before the dark misty night came on, then John left, whistling over the ice in the gathering gloom.

Each night she waited, and each night for a week and a day John came, the dashing figure of her dreams, to warm her blood on those cold February evenings.

On the ninth night, February 24th, 1814, darkness had come early but Lilian waited and soon her ears were rewarded by the rolling of the drum as her soldier whistled over the ice. But, to her cold horror, the drum roll was suddenly silenced by a terrific creak, a cracking splash .... and then silence.

Lilian's blood seemed to freeze, and she wailed a loud mourning howl, then waited, dementedly treading the marshy shore. Nothing. Lilian screamed, full of fear, then screamed again and again until her father, hearing her torment, came running. He carried his beloved daughter home to a desolation that took her years to overcome.

John Sadler's soul did not rest in peace, and on February nights, at the gloaming time, the figure of a phantom skater can still sometimes be seen, beating a roll on his drum, as he seeks out someone on the Heigham side of Hickling Broad.

DESPERATE DEFENCE AT WOODCROFT HOUSE

About seven miles south-east of Stamford, in the Cambridgeshire village of Etton, is Woodcroft House. It is a fine fortified manor, with the appearance of a castle, an atmosphere that inspired John Clare to write about it, and a past fit to send shivers down your spine.

Charles I was not the most popular of British monarchs. He held the belief that he had a Divine Right, as a king guided by God, to do as he felt best for the country. Others disagreed strongly, wondering what Parliament was for, if not to be consulted about making the laws of the land. Charles, an Anglo-Catholic, ruled Great Britain from 1625, and for eleven years he was the absolute monarch, not consulting parliament at all. Fierce opposition grew, especially on religious matters.

Things finally came to a head in 1640, in Scotland, because the severely suppressed Puritans staged a revolt. As a direct result of this the Long Parliament met and the King was at its mercy. Civil War was heralded by the King's standard being raised at Nottingham on August 22, 1642. Many battles raged, all over the land, with most of the population feeling strongly enough to take one side or the other. The Royalists were mainly led by Prince Rupert, a nephew of the King, and the Parliamentarians, or Roundheads, were led by General Fairfax and his kinsman, Oliver Cromwell, both from Cambridgeshire.

The King, of course, lost many of the battles and, eventually, his head, but this did not happen until January 1649. The year before this there was great excitement at Woodcroft House, a Royalist stronghold.

By 1648 the conflict seemed to be nearing its end and the

later skirmishes were often bitter and vindictive, with the Roundheads fiercely pursuing anyone still championing the Royalist cause.

One of the King's most ardent supporters was a Dr Hudson, who had been imprisoned for airing his anti-parliament views. He escaped from the Tower of London and headed for Lincolnshire where he met up with the Rev Mr Stiles. Together they raised a party of horsemen and headed for the comparative safety of Woodcroft House. Although they were attacked by roundhead troops, Dr Hudson and his men reached their destination and set about barricading themselves in. Some ventured out during their partial siege, in order to cheekily attack the Roundheads who were quartered in nearby Stamford.

Their impudence enraged Colonel Winters, the Parliamentarian commander, who ordered a reprisal attack on Woodcroft House, to be led by his brother-in-law. He intended to teach Hudson and the others a lesson that would at least keep them within their fortress. Winters was so confident of success that he was confounded when, just an hour later, the straggling remains of the troop returned with news that their leader had been killed.

With murder in his heart, Colonel Winters ordered his adjutant to rouse another troop which he would personally lead to Woodcroft House.

Dr Hudson and his friends, after their successful defence, were taking the chance to snatch a meal and replenish their armoury. Shocked by the speed of the second attack, the Royalists were thrown into complete disarray. Colonel Winters found it quite easy to actually enter the House and scatter its inhabitants to the four corners of the building. He announced loudly that any who surrendered would be dealt with lightly but not that rogue Hudson: the Doctor was not to be spared.

Some appeared from their hiding places, behind curtains and under furniture, but none had seen Dr Hudson or was prepared to suggest where he may be. A complete search of the building was ordered by the Colonel.

Dr Hudson actually stood behind an arras on the stairs of the Bastion Tower and was forced to flee when a Roundhead sword was plunged through the tapestry. Hudson leapt up the stairs, followed by the soldier, who had shouted out for help, rushed out through the windows on the top floor and onto the parapet of the battlements. He flung himself over, grasping the battlements firmly, intending to drop into the moat. The problem was that his pursuer was closer than he thought. The Roundhead had seen the spot where Hudson jumped over the parapet, dashed towards it and with a great swing of his sword, cut off Dr Hudson's hands cleanly at the wrists. The poor man fell, screaming, to the moat below and the noisily jubilant soldiers flew down the stairs and to the moat to pull him out. But not to rescue him! A soldier named Egborough knocked him on the head with his musket whilst another, Walker, who was a grocer in Stamford, cut out Dr Hudson's tongue.

By the time Colonel Winters arrived the doctor was dead and this dark episode in the history of Woodcroft Hosue was over.

Mr Walker kept Dr Hudson's tongue about his person for some time after deserting his business in favour of soldiering. He lost all his money and died a pauper - some form of retribution, I suppose, for his grisly deed.

Oliver Cromwell of Huntingdon

It is said that on the day Oliver Cromwell was born he held out his arms towards a tapestry depicting Satan beckoning to his imps. The midwife took this as a sign that "He is for the gallows in this world, and the fires of Hell in the next."

History has not been kind to Cromwell, for though he seems to have been a fair and just man of good intention, there are plenty of unpleasant stories attached to his name too.

Oliver Cromwell was born and educated in Huntingdon, worked in Ely for some time and was a public servant all of his life. As a member of parliament, he became disillusioned, if not sickened, by the way Charles I was ruling the country and vowed to do something about it. The pages of history books tell us about his involvement in the Civil War so all we need to say here is that Charles I was beheaded, Oliver Cromwell became 'The Protector' and leader of the people but the Royalists, or Cavaliers, did not rest. At the battle of Worcester on September 3, 1651, the Scots were defeated but the night before this Oliver Cromwell is said to have had a dream. The scene of the tapestry at his birth was re-enacted before him, and he promised Satan his life, after seven years, in exchange for victory. He won, and Puritan rule continued for eleven years, but Cromwell died of ague on September 3, 1658. Satan had taken that which had been promised to him.

Oliver Cromwell lay in Westminster Abbey for three years before being taken with other regicides, both dead and alive, to Tyburn to be hung, drawn and beheaded. His head was stuck on a spike in Westminster Hall where it stayed until it was stolen 27 years later! 100 years afterwards, this shrivelled horror was displayed in a museum but a few years ago it was presented to Sidney Sussex College in Cambridge and buried there. His soul does not rest in peace, but wanders still.

THE HAPPISBURGH SMUGGLER

The church on the cliff top at
Happisburgh thrusts its tall tower into
the lofty sky over the sea.
No doubt the sight of it gives solace to
the seafarers as they near home.
Its goodness is needed
closer to home, though, just down the hill
at the evil spot known as
Well Corner.

Sydney Baker came staggering out of Hill House Inn, just below the church at Happisburgh, practically overflowing with good country ale, and lurched down the stony incline on his way home. After the soft glow of the candles in the inn, Sydney's eyes took some time to get used to the fitful light of the moon as it played hide and seek in the cloudy sky. The only slight concern to blight Mr Baker's otherwise calm and happy mood was the thought of his wife's nagging the following morning. She was right, of course, he should not have stayed out so late with work to think about early in the morning. But a man needs some respite and Sydney had enjoyed such a pleasant time, that August evening in the year 1800, that he thought he could close his ears again to his wife's sharp words.

He felt just fine as he rolled on, past the old well and along the road, so what made him turn he did not know. Was it the fall of a stone, or the call of an owl? Whatever it was, Sydney stopped, turned and stood transfixed, shivering and gasping, unable to move, as a hideous form moved from the direction of the sea and closer, ever closer, to Sydney.

In the clear moments of monlight he saw it plainly: the figure of a man clutching a sack and wearing the clothes of a seafarer.

What made Sydney so afraid though, was the fact that the figure *glided* towards him, down the hill, because he had no legs! Coupled to this was the realisation, as Sydney could clearly see when the thing drew nearer, that its head lay backwards between its shoulders on a horrible strip of skin.

Suddenly sober, Sydney Baker began to gibber as the spectre came right up to him ...... but it passed by and continued until arriving at Well Corner. Reaching down the well, it first dropped the sack then glided down after it, thus disappearing from Sydney's view.

Hot and cold at the same time Sydney may have been, but his legs were just able to carry him homewards, with his eyes starting from his head and his whole frame practically rigid with terror. His wife was awoken by the banging of the door and began her tirade from her pillow. With lighted candle, she made her way down the stairs and saw Sydney standing there, chattering to himself in a nonsensical way. Sure that he was drunk, she stalked off to bed, pulling him along behind her.

The next morning Sydney would not get out of bed. At about 8.30 Mr Howes, his employer, came round to see what had happped to him, angry that the work was not being done. Normally Sydney was reliable, sound and sensible, so notice had to be taken of the story he told his employer that morning. In any case, Sydney was refusing to stir from his bed until the mystery had been solved.

Later on that day, Mr Howes met with three neighbouring farmers to discuss harvesting and mentioned Sydney's experience to them. The four agreed that they would visit the well that evening to see if the spirit would manifest itself again.

At 11pm that night these four good Norfolk gentlemen walked down the road towards the well and there they waited patiently. Half an hour later they all witnessed exactly the same sight that Sydney had experienced the night before! They were almost as shocked as Sydney had been, but they were sober. Not for long, for they retreated to Mr Howes' farmhouse and fortified themselves with good un-excised brandy as they animatedly discussed the night's events. The four decided to go back the next evening and see if the same same scene unfolded: it did, and the next night. By this time Mr Howes' brandy supply was diminishing and this reminded him of a rumour he had heard.

Mr Howes asked Sydney Baker and three others to go with him to the well early the next morning, and they took a long rope ladder with them. One man, braver than the rest, climbed down into the well while the others waited at the top. To the shock of all of the men apart from Mr Howes, a torso was brought up to the surface after the first sortie. The second trip down revealed a sack containing a head and a pair of legs. Once again Sydney's eyes were popping out but Mr Howes said that all would be explained soon, and it was.

It seems that the smugglers who delivered tax-free brandy to the gentry had quarrelled amongst themselves about the price of the booty. The one who came out worst from the negotiations, and ended up in the well, was a man from Sea Palling.

Sydney Baker gave up the drink that night and so will anyone else who lingers by Well Corner when the moon is right. For the smuggler still glides by, even though the old well was filled in years ago!

THE WELLS OF BAWBURGH

Saint Walstan is the patron saint of Agricultural Workers. He was born and buried in Bawburgh, near Norwich, and traces of his existence are there to this day. It is a pretty village on the River Yare, and there are wells in the area which have been wonderfully curative. This story is over a thousand years old but still can be wondered at today.

A hundred years before the Normans conquered England, the largest house in Bawburgh was occupied by a wealthy couple, Benedict and St Blide, who were related to the King. They had a son, Walstan, who showed promise of being a great scholar but his first love was for the land.

When he was fourteen years old, Walston greatly distressed his parents by telling them that he intended to renounce them, his learning and his inheritance and seek to serve God and the poor. The following day, Walstan dressed in old clothes and prepared to leave the house. He begged forgiveness of his mother and father and hoped for their blessing eventually, then set out to tred the dusty roads.

After just a few miles, Walstan reached Taverham where he met a farmer who was in need of a labourer. He reached an agreement with this man and from then onwards adopted the life of a landworker, with its long hours, backbreaking labour and primitive tools. It was a life that he loved though, finding a quiet but satisfying communion with the crops and animals, and deriving joy from the slow passing of the changing seasons. Walstan enjoyed meeting the few travellers who passed by, hearing their news and telling them of his own life and faith in the power and love of God. There were few opportunities for him to give to or to serve others as he was so poor himself, but one day a poor traveller came along the road, limping badly on his sore and unshod feet. Walstan stopped work to talk to the man and, on hearing that he was hungry, gave him the major share of his humble meal and then insisted on the stranger accepting a gift of his own shoes.

The farmer's wife was furious that Walstan had given his shoes away and sent him out to hoe the vegetable plot before giving him his supper. It should have taken two or three hours but within half an hour the task was not only completed but, as if by divine intervention, done well.

The farmer's wife was dumbfounded by this apparent miracle and treated him differently from then onwards.

After Walstan had served for many years, his master gave him a cart and two calves. They grew into two fine, friendly bulls and were trained to pull the cart, giving immense pleasure to Walstan as he grew older.

It is said that on May 27th, 1016, Walstan was visited by God and told that he had only three more days on earth. Walstan prepared for the end of his life, letting it be known that he should be placed in his oxen cart and buried wherever it was that they finally came to rest.

Walstan was working in a field by Taverham when he died and there welled from the earth a spring of pure water which enabled him to be given the sacrament of the last rites. The farmer placed Walstan's body reverently on his cart and the oxen set forth.

The journey took them through Costessy where they paused in the woods. A second spring of water gushed forth there and this one continued to give water until the end of the 18th Century. The oxen finally stopped at Bawburth, Walstan's birthplace and final resting place. It is said that they passed through the north wall of the church and, indeed, a third spring appeared there. It is to this spring that many miracles were ascribed.

Walstan's body was buried at the northern end of the church and a shrine was established over him. Present day visitors can still see traces of the shrine in the church wall, and the well is still there, although on private ground.

Walsingham Shrine

This world famous shrine is a few miles inland from the north Norfolk coast, and the modern church built there is a focus for pilgrims from both near and afar. The original shrine was built as the result of Richeldis de Fervaquere having a recurrent dream.

For three nights, in a dream, the lady was transported to Palestine and shown the room where the Archangel Gabriel visited Mary to tell her that she was to be the Mother of Jesus. Richeldis was to take careful note of the building and duplicate it in Walsingham. Builders, carpenters and materials were assembled before Richeldis realised that she had no indication of exactly where to build. There was a further divine message: after a heavy dew fall, two pieces of land remained quite dry in a meadow near to a pair of ancient wells. Building began on the land nearest the wells but it was difficult. Richeldis prayed for assistance and the next day a marvellous site met her eyes. The materials had been used and reassembled on the other dry spot in exactly the form Richeldis had seen in Palestine!

For many years, pilgrims worshipped in sight of the statue of Mary and Jesus that Richeldis had asked to be placed there, and miraculous cures were worked by the waters of the twin wells. Rich and poor made the journey, in their thousands, and one visitor was King Henry VIII, entering barefoot from the slipper chapel. Ironically, Henry was the one responsible for the destruction of the shrine in September 1534.

THE RED BARN MURDER

At Polstead, in Suffolk near to the Essex border, there was once a red barn with something of a mysterious air about it. It is said that the barn was stained red, signifying horror and murder, by the setting sun. This is a theory that can no longer be tested for the barn was pulled down quite recently, leaving behind just its mystery.

William Corder was a troublesome young man, from a wealthy landowning family, who had always been a thoroughly bad lot. It was no surprise to anyone when William was charged with murder, even though it was more prejudice than proof that led to his conviction.

Maria Marten, the daughter of a neighbour of the Corder's, had an illicit and tempestuous affair with William which resulted in a baby boy being born in Sudbury. He was not well and died while still an infant but this was not the only child that Maria had. From a previous relationship there was another son, Thomas Henry, and Corder was jealous of this healthy child.

The father of Thomas Henry, a Mr Matthews, was an honourable man and he sent a quarterly sum of money for the upkeep of his son. When one such payment did not arrive, Maria wrote to Mr Matthews and received a reply to say that he had, indeed, sent the money. Maria questioned the delivery driver and was told that William had intercepted the package, a charge that Corder did not deny. Theft was, in the days of the early 1800s, a hanging offence: Maria, therefore, had William in her power.

Maria and her son lived with her father and stepmother,

Annie, in quite a small cottage. Annie was envious of her husband's love for his daughter so when Maria started to talk of marriage to Corder, Annie encouraged her. The two plotted together and Maria had no idea that her stepmother disliked her so much.

The story that was told afterwards claimed that William was not so keen on the idea of marriage but Maria continuously cajoled and threatened him. He supposedly arranged to meet her in the Red Barn on the afternoon of May 17th, 1827. Maria was dressed in her travelling clothes and carried an umbrella, for she intended to ask William to marry her and planned to go away with him. If he refused she would threaten to report his theft to the constabulary.

It was said that a bitter quarrel took place, a gun appeared and in the tussle Maria was shot. William buried her body in a hole dug in the floor of the barn then audaciously, and seemingly without conscience, carried on with his life. He moved to London, saying he was afraid of catching consumption in the low damp fields of Suffolk, and wrote letters claiming to be living there with Maria.

Soon after Christmas, Maria's stepmother told her husband that she had dreamt that Maria was under the floor of the Red Barn. Annie was not taken seriously but she begged her husband to investigate and he eventually gave in, in late April. Mr Marten took his mole spade and, with other men, dug the barn floor up until his daughter's body was found. Mrs Marten told the constable that she had seen William Corder coming from the Red Barn with a pick axe on his shoulder, and Mr Marten said that Corder had been seen in church with Maria's umbrella.

William Corder was not in hiding so was quickly tracked down and thrown into prison.

Within weeks he was found guilty of the gross murder of Maria Marten and was sentenced to death. He was hanged on Monday, August 11th, 1828, at Bury St Edmonds jail.

During the trial he claimed that Maria had shot herself, but a surgeon testified that stab wounds had killed her. Why did not someone suggest that it may have been Mr Marten's mole spade that had caused the stab marks?

Before his death, however, Corder admitted his involvement in the murder and wrote:

I am guilty, my sentence is just, I deserve
my fate and may God have mercy on me.

But was he guilty, or was it the jealous stepmother? Was her precognitive dream real - or just a way of putting the blame elsewhere?

This is not the end of the story though, for a book about the trial was bound in Corder's skin and his skeleton was used for anatomy lessons at teaching hospitals. One doctor stole the skull when he left the area - thus taking Corder's ghost with him. He heard awful noises in his house and saw strange shadows. The poor doctor was terrorised and peace did not return to his home until skull was reunited with body!

The Battle of Sole Bay

Overlooking the cliffs at Southwold, on a green at the back of the houses, is a row of cannon, their muzzles pointing out to sea. They seem inappropriate in this genteel Suffolk resort, but they are a reminder of an incident in the town's history.

Sole Bay, just off Southwold, was the setting for a piece of heard but not seen history which took place on Whitsuntide Monday, May 28th, 1692. It might have been arranged by some entertainment committee, for here a great battle was fought between the French, English and Dutch fleets.

For weeks, French and English sailors had been seen ashore in Southwold, allies for once. The headquarters of James, Duke of York, Lord High Admiral of the Fleet, was at Sutherland House, and from here emanated talk of a third Dutch War. Indeed, fighting had taken place on the sea already, and some casualties had been brought ashore.

The allied fleet had 101 men-of-war anchored in the bay, plus fire ships and tenders, with 6,018 guns and 34,500 men. The Dutch had 168 ships altogether, including 91 men-of-war.

One of the three commanders, the Earl of Sandwich, was concerned that his fleet was vulverable to attack for they were not on full alert. Sandwich, notorious for his personal and political vices, was on good form on the foggy day the Dutch decided to attack by sending in fireships. To enable the rest to prepare themselves, Sandwich took his ship out of the bay to engage the enemy, thus saving many ships and lives. In the great sea battle that followed, he personally killed the Dutch Admiral, van Ghent, but his own ship, along with many others, went down and the valiant Earl lost his life.

The battle was neither won nor lost, but drawn, heard by the Southwold folk on the shore but, eerily, not seen because of the fog and the smoke from the blazing ships.

THE THREE PIPERS OF BECCLES

The little black and white Suffolk town
of Beccles clings tenaciously
to the River Waveney and nestles
up to Norfolk.
From this pretty spot
comes a strange and evil tale.
The Pied Piper of Hamelin story tells
of one instance
of a town being rid of rats, but here is another.

During the 17th Century the Black Death touched all of Western Europe with its deadly, diseased fingers. Beccles, at this time, was a small and thriving town with citizens of every type living in half-timbered buildings which were infested with rats aplenty. As the townsfolk tried to sleep at night, squeaking and scrabbling betrayed the rats existence, and real evidence of their dirty brown teeth and filthy feet was to be seen in store-rooms and larders.

The infestation became worse, to the point where people hated to go to bed, where dreams were disturbed by the movement of great hordes of rats. Old people and children were often bitten as they slept and many lived in fear, for they had heard that rats could spread disease.

The elders of the town, led by the Portreeve, were constantly being asked to do something about the rats, but they seemed powerless to solve the problem that affected them all.

One day as he sat in his room, three men sought an audience with the Portreeve. As they filed in, respectfully doffing their hats, the senior elder wondered what complaints they brought. The three were Peter Harris, watchmaker, Jonathan Betts, tallow chandler, and Samuel Partridge, a pedlar. Far from bringing more complaints, however, the three had a suggestion to make. Ordinary, simple, townsfolk though they seemed, these three believed that they could pipe the rats away from the town and destroy them! This was most extraordinary, but the Portreeve had nothing to lose, for they were not asking for payment until after their task had been completed.

The three men were asked to come back later in the day and messengers were sent out to summon the town meet. The elders and seniors gathered at the town hall, grumbling at the summons, and talking about the rats and funerals that were being organised. When the Portreeve entered the room, all talking ceased and the suggestion of the morning was put to them. No-one was particularly hopeful but agreed that they had nothing to lose and much to gain should Peter, Jonathan and Samuel be successful. 45,000 marks would be a fair price to pay, for the rats had already caused a lot of costly damage.

Down by the river, in a filthy decrepit shack, there lived three dreadful old hags, Nancy Driver, Sally Price and Fanny Barton. Always cackling, screaming and quarrelling, they made their dirty, muddy corner of the river a place of ill-repute. Sensible adults avoided it and children, fearful, would shun the area. The townsfolk had once asked the Portreeve to keep the three harridans in order and so he had been forced to visit them. Their language and behaviour disgusted him and he fled with their curses ringing in his ears. They willed the housewives' puddings to become filled with flies, and they were. The Portreeve kept his distance after that.

Rumour had it that the chief piece of furniture in their hut was a large iron cauldron into which anything, alive or dead, would vanish. It was this rumour that Peter, Jonathan and Samuel had in mind when they visited the Portreeve.

The three men had ventured down to the river to see the three witches, and courageouslay stayed long enough to make some sort of bargain with them about the destruction of the rats. Who can say what dealing and double-dealing took place.

So it was that on the 31st of August the inhabitants of Beccles watched with pleasure and anticipation as Samuel, Peter and Jonathan stood in the square and piped strange tunes which hung winsomely on the air. Then came the squeaking, rushing, pittering and pattering as thousands of rats came out of hiding places and over the cobbled streets.

The three men piped on and on, until every rat in town was there and then they turned and headed for the river, leading the swarming mass away. It was a terrible, but much welcomed, sight.

There was great rejoicing in Beccles that evening, and the next day not a rat, or even a mouse, was to be found. All had vanished, the cleaning up began and the door to the three hags' hut was firmly locked.

The Portreeve waited in his office, with 45,000 marks on his desk, but the pipers did not come to collect their well-earned reward. In fact, they never came, leaving quite a gap in the written history of Beccles, although Sheldon wrote about the event in 1642.

You may think that was the end of the story but you would be wrong: the spirits of the three men did not rest. Each year at sunset, on August 31st, the shrill notes of the three pipers can be heard on a bend in the river, just below the town.